The NASEN A–Z:
A Graded List of Reading Books

New Edition

by Mike Hinson and Charles Gains

A NASEN Publication

First published in 1993.
Revised edition published in 1997.

ISBN 0 906730 88 0

NASEN

Published by NASEN Enterprises Ltd.
NASEN Enterprises is a company limited by guarantee, registered in England and Wales.
Company No. 2637438.

Further copies of this book and details of NASEN's many other publications may be obtained from the Publications Department at its registered office:
NASEN House, 4/5 Amber Business Village, Amber Close, Amington, Tamworth, Staffs. B77 4RP.
Tel: 01827 311500; Fax: 01827 313005;
email: welcome@nasen.org.uk

Copy editing by Mike Hinson.
Cover design by Graphic Images.
Typeset in Helvetica by J. C. Typesetting.
Printed in the United Kingdom by Arkle Print, Northampton.

THE NASEN A–Z: A GRADED LIST OF READING BOOKS

Contents

Acknowledgements

The authors and publishers wish to express their gratitude to:

- many publishers for their information and generosity;
- Sheila Atherden and colleagues from the Sandwell Child Psychology Service for their invaluable help in assessing readability;
- Jeff Hughes for his advice on computer software;
- Chris Sawyer and Emma Knight for 'A fast method for calculating text readability levels', from *Support for Learning,* Vol 6, No 2, 1991.

THE NASEN A–Z: A GRADED LIST OF READING BOOKS REVISED EDITION

Introduction

Since the first edition of this handbook was published in 1993, the teaching of reading has continued to hit the headlines of national newspapers and be the subject of many debates (and arguments).

In *The National Curriculum*, published in 1995, the DfEE clearly sets out its general requirements for English at Key Stages 1-4. First and foremost, teachers are expected to develop pupils' abilities to communicate in speech and writing, to listen with understanding, and enable them to become 'enthusiastic, responsive and knowledgeable readers'. To achieve the latter, they should be taught to:

- 'read accurately, fluently and with understanding;
- understand and respond to the texts they read;
- read, analyse and evaluate a wide range of texts, including literature from the English literacy heritage and from other cultures and traditions'.

(paragraph 1b)

Reading at Key Stage 1

In order to stimulate enthusiasm at Key Stage 1, pupils are expected to have extensive experience of children's literature and be afforded opportunities to:

'... read on their own, with others and to the teacher, from a range of genres that includes stories, poetry, plays and picture books'.

(Key Stage 1 Reading, paragraph 1a)

The essential features of suitable reading resources are itemised and include: interesting subject matter; accessible themes and ideas; clarity of expression; language with recognisable repetitive patterns, rhyme and rhythm, and visually stimulating presentation.

With regard to the teaching of basic reading skills at Key Stage 1, the document emphasises the necessity for a balanced and coherent programme which includes phonic and graphic knowledge, word recognition, grammatical knowledge, the fostering of contextual understanding and the use of a range of information sources.

Reading at Key Stage 2

'Pupils should be encouraged to develop as enthusiastic independent and reflective readers. They should be introduced to a wide range of literature, and have opportunities to read extensively for their own interest, pleasure and information'.

(Key Stage 2 Reading, paragraph 1a)

At Key Stage 2, pupils are expected to be actively improving their ability to read with fluency, accuracy, understanding and enjoyment, also extending their phonic and graphic knowledge to include more complex patterns. They should be taught how to find information in books and computer-based sources and provided with opportunities to read for different purposes by adopting appropriate strategies for the task. These include skimming, scanning and reading in depth.

Reading Resources

Clearly, these basic tenets have implications for schools' reading resources. On the one hand, publishers have responded by producing what is probably the best ever range of reading materials. Recently published schemes closely follow the latest National Curriculum requirements and well-established programmes have been quick to develop the necessary additional items.

On the other hand, there is the question of funding. The Educational Publishers Council has recommended that 2 per cent of a school's annual budget should be spent on books. As a result of its 1993 survey, the Book Trust concluded that £35.77 per pupil per year would buy the bare minimum of class books needed in a primary school (of which £15.50 could be spent on English books). For secondary schools, the estimated figure rose to £47.55.

Overall, year by year, school budgets have become increasingly tight and these estimates may appear to be something of an ideal.

The NASEN A-Z List

The main purpose of this handbook is to facilitate the choice, prudent purchasing and organisation of reading resources in order that they can be effectively matched to the individual needs of young readers.

This new edition pays some attention to pre-reading materials. Although an important element in classroom early learning experiences, NASEN has not previously published a means of classifying them so that items can be used more effectively in devising pre-reading programmes. Charles Gains suggests a procedure in the first part of this handbook which could well herald a separate publication at some future date.

The majority of books listed in the main section have a readability level below 11 years, as the principle of *The NASEN A-Z: A Graded List of Reading Books* is to help improve basic reading skills. All titles are listed alphabetically. Based on current empirical information, each series has been allocated a Phase, an Interest Age and a Reading Level. The entire list has been carefully checked and some old and out-of-print titles, listed in the First Edition, have been deleted to make way for more recently published series. Nevertheless, it is recognised that schools need to foster 'good housekeeping' by making careful use of books which have recently gone out-of print but which are judged as still being viable.

Schools realise that a major factor in improving literacy standards is the provision of an adequate and varied selection of attractive pre-reading reading materials. As part of its language policy, every school needs to develop strategies for appraising its existing stock, for choosing and purchasing new stock, and then integrating both old and new stock into a readily accessible collection of reading resources. This handbook is intended to assist this process. It has a valuable part to play in ensuring that young readers' needs are effectively catered for and that they progress as smoothly as possible to an independent level of reading.

Mike Hinson

THE NASEN A–Z: A GRADED LIST OF READING BOOKS

Pre-reading Materials

Background and Rationale

Most children have little difficulty proceeding through the range of pre-reading materials and other stimulating activities towards competence in reading. However significant numbers stumble at these early hurdles and continue to have problems in reading throughout their school career. Clearly if they can be better prepared for the task there might be considerably fewer who subsequently come to find reading a difficult and unpleasant chore. Conscious of this early years teachers make a wide variety of flash cards, reading games, worksheets and so on to support their existing strategies. Special needs co-ordinators often help and advise in these tasks. Teachers also draw on a wide range of published material.

In this latter respect publishers have increasingly become more sophisticated in analysing and developing materials that prepare and ease the process of reading and other basic skills. However, there remains no standard means of classifying such pre-reading materials in the way this publication grades books in respect of their readability. The reasons are fairly obvious and relate to the variety and complexity of that which is produced and sold. It also relates to what constitutes a range of 'pre-reading' skills and experiences. This is a controversial area and one that does not lend itself for debate here. Suffice to say we use the term 'pre-reading' only because of its common usage and as a means of roughly identifying the range of skills traditionally deemed necessary as a precursor to handling text.

Although there have been some attempts to classify the range of activities (eg Gains CW and Pritlove SA, (1985) *The Humberside Early Learning Project,* Humberside LEA), efforts in this direction have usually foundered because individual published items often achieve more than one end. An approximation is the best one can expect and the 'clustering' strategy as advocated here presents the best way of giving some means of ordering activities and ensuring key skills are not overlooked.

The rationale behind the gradation of activities of any sort lies in the field of mastery learning, as advocated by a number of leading authorities but in particular Benjamin Bloom. Such theorists maintain that most learning tasks are hierarchical and sequenced. Children following such paths will not only have their learning accelerated but this will have a very positive effect on their confidence and self-image. Briefly, the operational principles of mastery learning are as follows:

- Tasks should be broken down into small learning units and systematically arranged;
- Each unit should be mastered before proceeding;
- Feedback to the learner on success or otherwise should be given on completion of each unit;
- Where there is failure or less than complete mastery original material should be supplemented with 'correctives' ie alternative ways of presenting the task.

Although the above applies to learning generally it is particularly important to children with learning difficulties who will need long periods of structured and monitored experiences.

Skill clusters

For the purposes outlined we have come to the conclusion that pre-reading activities are best dealt with in clusters, not only for convenience but in order to relate to National Curriculum demands. To this end we offer the following clusters of pre-reading skills:

Discrimination and Writing Tasks

This relates to those areas that promote:

- Tactile awareness;
- Visual discrimination;
- Visuo-motor and handwriting.

Listening and Word Building

This relates to areas that promote:

- Auditory discrimination, memory and sequencing;
- Phonic awareness, sounds, blends and sequencing;
- Early spelling acquisition.

Language and Reading

This relates to areas that promote:

- Expressive language;
- Receptive language;
- Word and sentence recognition;
- Comprehension.

Thinking Skills

This relates to areas that promote:

- Thinking;
- Sequencing;
- Memory;
- Problem solving.

The above offers a general means of identifying and classifying published material and will bring some order to existing arrangements.

Grading Materials

The task of grading materials is not simple and needs to be conducted over a reasonable period of time. For example, teachers might include it as part of their development days. It also needs to be handled in a group situation so that teachers are aware of the different and sometimes more creative ways of handling particular activities and extracting the most value from them. A procedure might be as follows:

1. Select an activity that appears to meet a particular area of need.
2. Read what the publisher suggests.
3. Handle the activity, perhaps in a simulated fashion, and decide whether it meets the criteria stated. Publishers tend to make fairly generous predictions about their products!
4. Decide the **primary objective** of the task and classify it according to the four areas described above.
5. Decide if there is a useful **secondary objective** that might be usefully extracted at the same time.

6. Note any teaching procedures that should be followed to maximise the effect of the task.
7. Colour code the activity, for example:
   * Discrimination and Writing ....red
   * Listening and Word Building ....green
   * Language and Reading......................yellow
   * Thinking Skills ....blue
8. Next decide the level of the task, ie basic (1), standard (2), advanced (3) and also code. For example:
   Beads and Pattern Card Set (Philip and Tacey) might be classified as **Discrimination and Writing at Level 1**. The activity would be given a red sticker and the number 1 would be written on it.
   What's wrong? (LDA) might be classified as **Developing Thinking at Level 2**. It would therefore receive a blue sticker with a number 2 written on it.

The above procedure is somewhat arbitrary in as much as there will be disagreements among individual teachers as to the precise nature of a task. However, over a period of time it has been observed that as discussions among staff become more sophisticated a convergence of views frequently occurs.

It is obvious that if the above is computerised and developed over a period of time not only can charts be produced but a teachers manual is possible.

Advantages of grading pre-reading material

1. In attempting this task debates among staff clarify and inform generally about the nature of pre-reading.
2. The collation of material in this way identifies areas where there is insufficient support and informs about future purchases or the production of self-made aids.
3. Cross class methods become better standardised and integrated with other approaches.
4. Records of progress become more precise as failure in specific areas is more easily identified.
5. Continuity is more effectively achieved.
6. New members of staff find it easier to adjust to school methods and approaches.
7. Additional support in the shape classroom assistants, parental help etc can be better targeted.

Using the materials

Publishers' packaging often leaves much to be desired and staff might find it preferable to switch the majority of the materials to clear plastic zip wallets with the coding in a specific corner. This makes it considerably easier to store in boxes and on trolleys. The latter procedure also enables materials to be wheeled to groups or other classes as timetables dictate.

Wherever possible children themselves should have responsibility for controlling the operation and recording their own progress. *Figure 1* gives an example of such a procedure. Clearly all this is initially time-consuming but becomes quicker and more efficient over a period of time.

It is recommended that children work through 'clusters' of activities at the appropriate level and should cover **all** areas before moving up a level. The time spent on a cluster of activities is a matter of professional judgement and childrens' progress can be adjusted according to the rapidity or otherwise of their mastery. Working within a cluster of activities allows for mutual reinforcement and, in mastery terms, correctives.

Summary

Grading and using materials in this way is far from rigid and no two teachers will operate in precisely the same way. The flexibility of the system is its strength. Working through activities in this semi-structured way gives children and staff a great deal of confidence. Also as it is added to and adjusted over a period of time it becomes more effectively integrated into existing school language policies and strategies.

Charles Gains

STAGES IN THE USE OF PRE-READING MATERIALS

STAGES		CHILD'S ROLE	TEACHER'S ROLE	NOTES
EXPLORATION	1	COLLECT ITEM	SUPERVISE	Easy accessibility is important. Child learns - structure - order - sequencing
	2	RETURN AND REMOVE FROM WALLET		A drill to be established for … - removing - handling - use of space
	3	STREET		Five minutes to … STOP - THINK REASON - EXPLORE EXPLAIN THE TASK
OPERATION	4	DISCUSS WITH TEACHER	DISCUSS WITH CHILD	What has been discovered? Language is: - encouraged - deployed - developed
	5	TASK(S) EXPLAINED	TASK(S) EXPLAINED	Specific task(s) explained - practice - check - practice
	6	TASK(S) ATTEMPTED		Minimal supervision.
EVALUATION	7	TASK(S) CHECKED	TASK(S) CHECKED	Tasks checked. Decision. - go on - repeat - corrective
	8	RECORDING		Record card completion. Possible further written work, e.g. drawing, copying, to reinforce.
	9	ITEM RETURNED	SUPERVISE	Materials returned. Further practice in structure, order and sequencing.

⟷ DIRECT INTERACTION ← - - - - OCCASIONAL SUPERVISION

C. W. Gains
© 1997

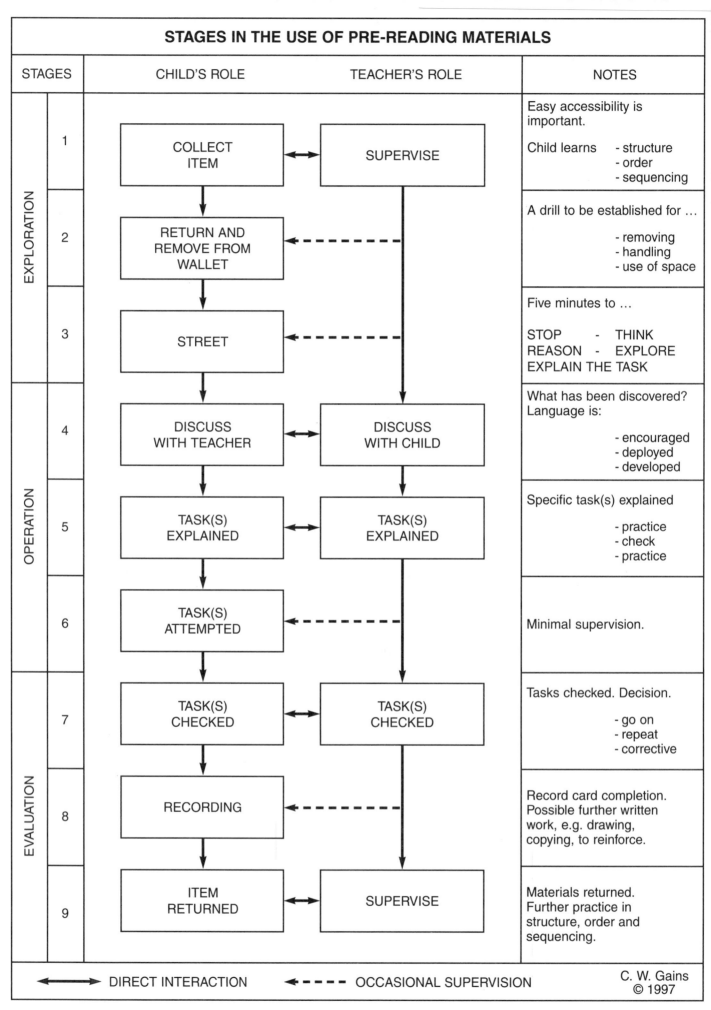

Figure 1 - Stages in the use of pre-reading materials.

THE NASEN A–Z: A GRADED LIST OF READING BOOKS

Towards a Reading Strategy

In order to sustain and advance reading levels a number of objectives are indicated. These are:

1. As wide a range of reading material as possible should be made available to pupils.
2. The material should be graded for readability to ensure as accurate a 'match' as possible between reader and text.
3. Reading progress should be regularly checked by a variety of methods including hearing pupils read and recording progress.
4. Individual difficulties should be immediately identified and corrected.
5. Opportunities for extending and widening reading should be readily available.

Schools frequently have to construct, or rewrite, their reading policies along these lines. This is of particular importance when significant numbers of pupils are identified as having learning difficulties. What follows is a step-by-step guide towards the implementation of such a strategy that will go some way towards helping schools maximise their resources and materials. It is usefully read alongside other NASEN publications and articles in the journals of the Association.

STEP 1 - THE AUDIT

- Collect information on pupils' performance including reading scores.
- Collate and interpret these results using a Class Survey of Reading Attainment chart *(Figure 2).*
- Where appropriate transfer the numbers to a School Survey of Reading Attainment chart *(Figure 3).*
- Collect and classify material as reading schemes, supplementary readers and series to encourage independent reading.
- The books listed in this handbook are grouped according to readability in six month levels as follows:

  A 5.0 - 5.5

  B 5.6 - 5.11

  C 6.0 - 6.5

  D 6.6 - 6.11

  E 7.0 - 7.5

  F 7.6 - 7.11

  G 8.0 - 8.5

  H 8.6 - 8.11

  I 9.0 - 9.5

  J 9.6 - 9.11

  K 10.0 - 10.5+

Letter, or colour code, as above. This system of letter/colour coding can be further extended by six monthly stages, as necessary.

- Review staff skills and availability.
- Identify other possibilities of help and support.
- Review the 'logistics' of delivery.

STEP 2 - STRUCTURE AND DELIVERY

- Prepare reading schedules based on the number of times per week a pupil should be heard read (use *Figure 2*). As a rough guide the following is suggested:

20% or more behind chronological age	-	5 times per week;
10% or more behind chronological age	-	3 times per week;
Within 10% plus or minus of chronological age	-	Twice per week;
Above 10% of chronological age	-	Once per week.

- Carefully timetable to ensure the above is carried out.
- Begin hearing pupils read using an agreed procedure.
- Check and record progress, preferably in collaboration with the pupil and in an attractive way.

STEP 3 - EXPAND AND INVOLVE

- Involve parents in home reading programmes whenever possible.
- Involve other adults and assistants in on-site support.
- Involve other pupils in 'peer tutoring'.

STEP 4 - INDIVIDUAL DIFFICULTIES

- Diagnose individual difficulties.
- Construct individual programmes for those who require particular help.
- Maximise the use of appropriate information technology to support all pupils, especially those individuals who are at risk.

STEP 5 - DEVELOPMENT

- Encourage comprehension and the understanding of text.
- Extend reading skills.
- Promote study skills.

The above does not necessarily indicate a linear progression but simply the broad elements which should be kept in mind in the construction of suitable strategies.

CLASS SURVEY OF READING ATTAINMENT

SCHOOL ......Brightview Primary......

YEAR ......4...... TEACHER ......Miss J...... DATE ......September......

A **5^{0}-5^{5}**	**B** **5^{6}-5^{11}**	**C** **6^{0}-6^{5}**	**D** **6^{6}-6^{11}**	**E** **7^{0}-7^{5}**	**F** **7^{6}-7^{11}**	**G** **8^{0}-8^{5}**	**H** **8^{6}-8^{11}**	**I** **9^{0}-9^{5}**	**J** **9^{6}-9^{11}**	**K** **10^{0}-10^{5}+**	
Peter 5^{2} Malcolm 5^{4} Gail (No score)	Edward 5^{9}	Abdul 6^{3} Jane 6^{4}	Mark 6^{9} Susan 6^{8} Emma 6^{8}	Rachel 7^{4} Yvonne 7^{0} Winston 7^{2}	Dennis 7^{8} John 7^{7} William 7^{8} Kim 7^{9} Kathleen 7^{6} Tina 7^{9} Robert 7^{7}	Steven 8^{3} Heather 8^{3} Jennifer 8^{5}	Kevin 8^{7} Gary 8^{9} Santok 8^{9}	Adrian 9^{0} Lesley 9^{4} Dawn 9^{2}	Balbir 9^{7} Brett 9^{9} Sarah 9^{9}	Catherine 10^{4} Pritpal 10^{1}	David 11^{2} Keith 12^{4}
Severe learning difficulties. Unlikely to make much headway without specialist attention. Individual educational programmes are essential.		Low average performance. Requires daily reading practice and supplementary activities. Close monitoring essential.		Within the average range of ability for Year 4 pupils. However still require regular practice and checking two to three times per week.				High average. Good performance but still require a weekly check on progress.		Very good scores. Capable of unsupervised work with occasional checks.	
						Will benefit from an organised programme of activities designed to improve reading fluency.					

Comments

The above chart is easily compiled, either by hand or as a computer printout. It can be helpful for seeing at a glance:

- the overall pattern of a class's reading attainments;
- the individual and relative positions of pupils;
- simple diagnostic comments (as illustrated above);
- the composition of reading groups;
- particular individuals who require specific attention and, possibly, special reading resources;
- the overall pattern of pupils' current and future reading book requirements.

The retention of these charts as a comparison of progress after subsequent re-testing can be extremely useful.

Figure 2 - A chart showing the reading distribution for a Year 4 class.

SCHOOL READING PROFILE

SCHOOL ....Brightview School........ DATE ....September 199-........

	Year Group	A	B	C	D	E	F	G	H	I	J	K	L	M	N	O	P	Q	R	Total Pupils	At risk	Average	Above Average
	Reading levels	5^{0}-5^{5}	5^{6}-5^{11}	6^{0}-6^{5}	6^{6}-6^{11}	7^{0}-7^{5}	7^{6}-7^{11}	8^{0}-8^{5}	8^{6}-8^{11}	9^{0}-9^{5}	9^{6}-9^{11}	10^{0}-10^{5}	10^{6}-10^{11}	11^{0}-11^{5}	11^{6}-11^{11}	12^{0}-12^{5}	12^{6}-12^{11}	13^{0}-13^{5}	13^{6}+				
		Average		Above average																			
Infant	1	16	11	5	4	0	2	1	2												%	27 / 66%	14 / 34%
Infant	2	8	10	7	3	4	4	1	5	1											%	28 / 65%	15 / 35%
Junior	3	4	7	5	2	9	5	1	7	2	3	1	1								11 / 23%	21 / 45%	15 / 32%
Junior	4	1	2	2	10	5	4	10	3	1	5	3	3	0	1						15 / 30%	22 / 44%	13 / 26%
Junior	5	0	0	4	5	3	3	4	6	2	4	4	3	2	3	2	2				15 / 32%	16 / 34%	16 / 34%
Junior	6	0	0	0	2	1	3	2	8	4	0	4	3	1	6	3	2	1	2		16 / 38%	11 / 26%	15 / 36%
Secondary	7																				%	%	%
Secondary	8																				%	%	%
Secondary	9																				%	%	%
		Below average and at risk														Average							

Comment:
The chart is useful for comparing the spread of reading skills within a school. The numbers of children are calculated from the Class Survey Chart and inserted in the appropriate box. The heavy lines indicate above average and 'at risk' pupils. This can be converted into percentages as indicated for finer comparison.

The chart is useful for

- establishing particular groups or classes 'at risk';
- targeting resources to alleviate difficulties;
- monitoring progress to ensure individuals and groups do not fall behind;
- planning the school's reading resources.

The results should be treated with some caution particularly where dissimilar tests have been used.

Figure 3 - This shows the spread of reading attainment in a primary school. While the percentage of pupils who are above average remains reasonably stable, the percentage of those at risk increases substantially.

Choosing Reading Books

In order that they should make the most effective use of the financial resources available, it is advisable for schools to develop a policy for buying books.

When considering new book resources, it is preferable to actually handle and examine potential purchases. Most LEAs have still managed to retain resource collections, often supervised by a support service or the schools' library service, or based in a teachers' centre. Book exhibitions continue to be organised by publishers. For example, NASEN is co-organiser with the Educational Publishers Council of several special needs exhibitions, held in London, at Haydock Park and other venues. A wide range of reading materials is displayed. A visit, certainly by the headteacher and the language and special needs co-ordinators, would prove well worthwhile when choosing new reading materials.

Books for the whole school

When selecting books, it is important to assess not only the strengths and weaknesses of a particular title or series, but also to be aware of that book's value in relation to the remainder of the school's reading resources. In order to reflect a balance, teachers should ask themselves if the entire collection includes:

- an adequate range of books with regard to both the reading curriculum and children's wider interests;
- a variety of books which are appropriate to children's different ages, abilities and reading attainments;
- books which cater for the needs of special groups within the school;
- books which reflect equal opportunities and a multicultural society.

In the process of making a final choice, the views of potential readers and of their parents might prove crucial.

Criteria for choosing books

Through the subliminal influence of modern mass media, children's tastes in reading materials have become increasingly sophisticated. When appraising potential additions to the school's book stock, a number of key questions need to be answered:

- Will the cover design and outward appearance of a book motivate the reader to open its pages?
- Does the size and style of print, and the space between words and lines, enable the book to be easily read?
- Are the illustrations of good quality? Will they help readers to understand the text?
- Is there an appropriate balance of text in relation to the illustrations?
- Is the book written in a clear style of language:
  - does it contain many unfamiliar words?
  - are there many long sentences?
  - how complex is the grammar? For example, are passive verbs used more than active verbs?
  - are ideas clearly organised?
- If it is a fiction book:
  - does it have a good story that will capture the reader's attention?
  - are the characters believable?
  - will readers be able to identify with the story?
- If it is a non-fiction book:
  - is the information up-to-date?
  - is the subject matter sufficiently simplified without being patronising?
  - are technical terms clearly explained?
  - is the information easily accessible (clear contents page, good index)?
- Are children with special needs portrayed in a sensitive way?
- Does the book contain any examples of racial stereotyping or sexism?
- Can the book be read out loud (does it sound good)?
- Would it merit rereading?
- Will the book have a reasonable shelf life?
- Is it durable and able to withstand reasonable classroom wear and tear?

Schools can easily simplify, or elaborate on, the above list.

THE NASEN A–Z: A GRADED LIST OF READING BOOKS

Assessing the Readability of Books

As long ago as 1975, the Bullock Report, *A Language for Life,* pointed out that a teacher's first step in planning instruction to meet specific needs is to assess the attainment level of every child and provide each with reading material of the right level of readability.

A teacher's authoritative knowledge of the relative reading levels of a wide selection of books can be a crucial factor in the process of matching any pupil to a book that he or she is able to read with both enjoyment and improved fluency.

The three techniques used in ascertaining a book's ***readability*** - or the ease with which it can be read are:

- through professional judgement;
- by the use of cloze procedure;
- by the use of a readability formula.

Professional judgement

Research studies (such as Harrison, 1980) have demonstrated that, working individually, teachers are not always reliable in their assessments of text difficulty. On the other hand, when several teachers pool their assessments of the readability of a particular book, then these tend to coincide.

Formal or informal discussions are an important part of assessing and purchasing new book stock. Joint discussion encourages a sense of 'ownership' and is likely to lead to a more consistent approach to classroom use.

Cloze procedure

Cloze procedure is, in effect, a systematic approach to 'filling-in the missing word'. Although time-consuming, this method can be effective when used to assess a particular title intended for general use, for example a subject textbook for pupils in a class or a year group.

A short passage, or series of passages, is chosen from the book and prepared in advance by deleting every fifth, seventh or tenth word. Pupils are then asked to fill in the missing words by using ones which they think the author might have used. The more correct answers given for each deleted word, the easier the text and the more easy it will be for the class or year group to use (see Bormuth, 1966).

Readability formulae

Readability formulae are usually based on statistical data. According to Colin Harrison, in his book *Readability in the Classroom* (Cambridge University Press, 1980), a good readability formula should have three attributes: it must be valid, reliable and easy to use.

The reading levels of the new materials included in this handbook have been calculated using the *Fry Readability Graph* (1968). Already familiar to many readers, this has proved its usefulness over the years and is applicable to materials intended for a wide range of purposes and age groups. The Fry Graph gives a reasonably accurate estimate of the difficulty of a book based on vocabulary and sentence length. It must be stressed that the procedure does not take into account: the typeface and size of print; the quality of the illustrations and layout of the pages; the intellectual demands that the text makes on the reader, or the author's style of writing.

Readability in the classroom

In *Support for Learning* (Vol 6, No 2, 1991), Sawyer and Knight published a fast method for calculating the readability of texts in BBC BASIC using the BBC Micro computer. This program has proved to be both simple and effective and can be used on other computers. It may be freely copied and adapted, and is reproduced in Appendix 1 on page 116. Several other programs which are commercially available are listed in Appendix 2.

For those readers who do not have access to computers, their best course of action would be to consult Harrison's book and to choose a formula most suited to their needs. The procedure for using each is explained in the text.

There is no mystique about calculating readability levels. The *NASEN A-Z* List is for quick reference and readers are at liberty to add their own calculations to it.

THE NASEN A–Z: A GRADED LIST OF READING BOOKS

Matching the Book to the Reader

Many young readers are capable of sifting through a varied collection of books and choosing something suitable to their current reading purposes. Others are equally motivated by the freedom of being allowed to choose for themselves, but appreciate the security of making that choice from a slightly more controlled range of books.

Whether books are part of a scheme or a separate series of supplementary readers, all of those listed in the *A-Z* under a particular letter grade have a similar readability level. Organising reading material in this way has several advantages:

- the pupil can choose from a variety of different titles of comparable reading difficulty;
- some readers need more practice at a particular level than others. The variety of titles at each grade helps to ensure that they do not become bored in the process;
- at whichever level a pupil starts, the letter grades are arranged to give positive progress;
- schools will usually require fewer copies of each title. This should help them to purchase a wider range of books for a similar outlay.

Once a school has:

- completed an audit of its reading resources;
- lettered (or colour-coded) its main reading scheme, supplementary reading books and new stock;
- arranged a conveniently located reading resource area, and
- ensured that pupils and teachers understand the way in which the system works,

the matching process between reader and book becomes straightforward.

Initially, it is advisable to allocate the reader to a letter grade which is one step below his or her current reading level, thereby ensuring that the first book is read with ease. This morale-booster promotes rapid progress to the next, slightly more difficult grade.

Operating the System

At each level, pupils are motivated because they are able to choose a title which interests them. Nonetheless, the operation of the system remains firmly in the hands of the teacher.

As the result of careful monitoring of reading progress, it will be the class teacher who decides when a child is ready to move on to the next letter grade. No reader should be left marking time once he or she is ready to move on, nor left struggling on a book which is too difficult. Doubtless, teachers and readers will be able to set mutually agreed targets during reading conferences. Hearing pupils read and careful recording and monitoring of their progress is an essential part of any reading programme.

THE NASEN A–Z: A GRADED LIST OF READING BOOKS

The Graded List of Reading Books
(collated and edited by Mike Hinson)

The books included in this list are mainly reading schemes or programmes and series of supplementary readers, together with some library and information books. A unique feature of the *A-Z List* is that it is out of date as soon as it is published. Educational publishing is so fiercely competitive that publishers are constantly bringing out new materials. The information included is as up-to-date and accurate as possible but is by no means exhaustive.

During the lengthy process of revising, it was noticed that an increasing number of 'resource' collections or boxes of children's paperback books are now on the market. Sometimes, these contain titles from more than one publisher and substitute titles are introduced into the collections on a fairly frequent basis. The authors have concluded that such collections are beyond the scope of this book. Nonetheless, such collections are a useful resource and can represent value for money. For this reason, additional blank charts are included at the back and details are given of computer programs which teachers can use to assess the readability of such books.

Key

O/P - books which have gone out-of-print, usually within the last five years.
T - a Teacher's Handbook is available (and is essential reading for all users).
S - supplementary materials (covering workbooks, work cards, worksheets, copymasters, flash cards, Language master cards, friezes, games, other activities, models - and so on).
AU - audio-tapes are available.
V - there is a video-tape.
IT - computer software.
RR - there are books for reading together.

PLEASE NOTE

The inclusion of a title or series does not imply a recommendation by the authors or publishers of this handbook. Whilst every care has been taken in the compilation of this list, the authors and publishers cannot accept any responsibility for any inaccuracies or changes since compilation.

The authors and publishers regret that they are unable to answer telephone queries about this list. Written queries should be addressed to: NASEN A-Z, NASEN House, 4/5 Amber Business Village, Amber Close, Tamworth, B77 4RP. and should include a stamped addressed envelope for a reply. Queries will be dealt with in strict rotation. Constructive comments about the book are always welcomed.

A

Title and Publisher	PHASE*	INTEREST AGE	Reading Level A 5^0-5^5	B 5^6-5^{11}	C 6^0-6^5	D 6^6-6^{11}
Action Series Hodder and Stoughton	P/S	11 - 16				
Action History Hodder and Stoughton	S	11 - 14				
All Aboard Ginn (T, S, AU, V, IT, RR)	P	4 - 6	**Core Reading** **Stage 1** Sam and Rosie Introductory Books (6), Sam and Rosie (8) titles, Pattern and Rhyme Introductory (6 books), Pattern and Rhyme (4 books), Non-Fiction Introductory (6 books), Non-Fiction (6 books), ← **Stage 2** → (A–B) Sam and Rosie Set A (8 books) Set B (4 books), Pattern and Rhyme Set A (4 books) Set B (4 books), Non-Fiction (6 books),	**Stage 3** Sam and Rosie Set A (8 books) Set B (4 books), Pattern and Rhyme Set A (4 books) Set B (4 books), Non-Fiction (6 books), ← **Stage 4** → (B–C) Sam and Rosie (4 books), Pattern and Rhyme (4 books), Non-Fiction (6 books),	**Stage 5** Sam and Rosie (4 books), Pattern and Rhyme (4 books), Non-Fiction (6 books),	Stage Sam and Rosie (4 books), ← Pattern (4 ← Stage Sam and Rosie
All Sorts (O/P) Cambridge University Press	P	6 - 9				
Alpha Books Oxford University Press	S	12 - 18				
Always in Trouble (O/P) Hodder and Stoughton	P/S	11 - 16				
Anglia Young Books Anglia Young Books	P	7 - 11				
Animals on the Move Ginn	P/S	8 - 13				

*P = Primary; S = Secondary

E 7^0-7^5	F 7^6-7^{11}	G 8^0-8^5	H 8^6-8^{11}	I 9^0-9^5	J 9^6-9^{11}	K 10^0-10^5+
		← Into Action, Join the Action, Action Replay, Action Stations, All Action,	→	Call to Action,		
				Medieval Times 1: The Invaders, Medieval Times 2: Medieval Times,		
6 and Rhyme books), → Non-Fiction (6 books), 7 (4 books) → **Stage 8** ← Sam and Rosie (4 books)	← **Stage 7** Pattern and Rhyme (4 books), Non-Fiction (6 books), → ← Pattern and Rhyme (4 books)	→ → → ← Non-Fiction (6 books)	→			
← A Wet Dinner Time, A Foggy Christmas, The Rubbish Dumpers, The Wedding, Abrar's Holiday, Joseph and his Jointed Camel,	→					
					← 1000 headwords level: The Lady Vanishes, Quiet as a Nun, The Poseidon Adventure, I Lucifer, True Grit,	→
← Always in Trouble, Still in Trouble, (for reading and writing)	→					
	Key Stage 1 History Quick Read Books 1-8		← Geography Quick Read Books 1-4	→ **Key Stage 2 History** Mission from the March, Rebels of the Fields,	Learn About the Saints, Learn About Festivals, Learn About Inventors, The Fox in the Wood, Royal Escape, Under the Rose, Flight of the Mallard, Charge to Victory, Escape from the Workhouse, Bow Street Runner,	The Discus Thrower, The Boy from Burnham Thorpe, The Plague Piper, Where the Frigate Flies, The Haunted Coast, Saxon Superman, Son of Rebellion,
		← Shape and Movement in Animals, Why Do Animals Move? Walking and Running, Jumpers and Hoppers, Climbers and Creepers, Animals in Water, Animals in the Air,	→			

A

Title and Publisher	PHASE*	INTEREST AGE	Reading Level A 5^0-5^5	B 5^6-5^{11}	C 6^0-6^5	D 6^6-6^{11}
Animal Stories (Series 497) (O/P) Ladybird	P	5 - 9				
Around and About (O/P) Ginn	P	5 - 7		At School, At the Fair, In the Garden, At the Seaside, Out Shopping, In the Street,		

B

Title and Publisher	PHASE*	INTEREST AGE	Reading Level A 5^0-5^5	B 5^6-5^{11}	C 6^0-6^5	D 6^6-6^{11}
Balloons (O/P) Ginn	P	5 - 7	← Balloons, Races, Clowns, Winter Walk, My Button Colours, →			
Bananas Heinemann	P	7 - 11				
Blue Bananas Heinemann	P	7 - 11				
Bangers and Mash Longman	P	5 - 10		1. The Hat Trick, 2. Eggs,	3. Wiggly Worms, 4. The Clock, 5. The Best Duster, 6. In a Jam, **Supplementary Readers** Hatching is Catching, Jumpers, Bubble Bath, Tea Break, Garden Trouble, The C.P.O.,	7. Ding Dong Baby, 8. Red Indians, 9. The Bee and the Sea 10. Wet Paint,
Beacon Reading (some O/P) Ginn	P	5 - 9	Kitty and Rover,	1. Part 1 At Home, **Library Books** ← Old Friends, →	1. Part 2 At Play,	2. Part 1 Old Dog Tom, ← Clever Folk, Folk
Beans A and C Black	P/S	8 - 14				

E 7^0-7^5	F 7^6-7^{11}	G 8^0-8^5	H 8^6-8^{11}	I 9^0-9^5	J 9^6-9^{11}	K 10^0-10^5+
			← Tasseltip Plays Truant, ...Takes a Ride, ...Buys a Present, ...Has a Lucky Day, ...Saves the Day, ...and the Boozle, ...Hannibal on Holiday, ...Runs Away, ...on the Nature Trail, ...and the Pet Show, →			
	Set 1 Freckle Juice,	Jane and the Pirates,	The Big Stink,	Dragon Trouble,		The Moon Monsters, The Ghost Child,
	Set 2	Lightening Fred,		Storm, Imp, Scaredy-Cat, Who's a Clever Girl Then?		The Disappearing Granny,
	Set 3 Yob,	No Guns, No Oranges, The Phantom Carwash,				Beware Princess, Brenda the Bold, How Jennifer (and Speckle) Saved the Earth,
	Set 4			Crocodile Dog, The No-So-Clever Genie?,	Snotty and the Rod of Power,	The Quest of the Golden Dragon, Debbie and the Little Devil Conker,
	Set 5	Dracula's Daughter,	The Beast in the Basement,		Ziggy and the Ice Ogre,	The Evil King's Daughter, Sasha and the Bicycle Thieves, Oh Paul!
	Set 6 Ollie Oddbin's Skylark, Squonk, Burper,			Polly Pipes Up,		Mermaid and Chips, You Herman, Me Mary,
	Set 7 Yummy Yuk, Walking the Goldfish,	The Monster from Under the Ground, The Ghost of Jigger Jack,	Planet of the Jumping Beans,		Jupiter Boots,	
	Set 8					Nancy Pockett and the Kidnappers, Snow Girl, Colly's Barn, Design a Pram, Spooky Cottage, The Big Red Trouble,
	Set 9 Horace and Morris, Alice's Magic Alice Band,	Wanting a Little Black Gerbil,	Something Big,	The Unicorn Dream, The Marble Crusher,		
The Nut Map, Baby Bear Comes Home, Big Dog and Little Dog Visit the Moon,	Dilly and the Goody-Goody, Juggling with Jeremy, Tom's Hat,					
11. Toothday and Birthday, 12. Bikes and Broomsticks, 13. The Hole Story, 14. The Cow and the Bull, Snatch and Grab Sticky Trousers	15. Back to School, 16. Knots and Knocks, 17. Kippers and Cleaners, 18. Tears and Cheers,					
2. Part 2 Little Chick Chick, Tales and Fancies, →	3. The Pancake, The Wise Little Goat, The Dragon Princess, The Golden Fish,	4. Careful Hans, Annancy Stories, The Faithful Beasts,	5. Briar Rose, The Emperor's New Clothes, The Seven Proud Sisters, Twelve Little Plays,	6. William Tell, The Lion and the Saint, The Winged Horse, The Bronze Mirror,		
				History: The Blacksmith's Horse, Jubilee Terrace, Vikings, **People at Work:** Bakery, Carpenter, The Vet, Lorry Driver (Fishing Boat, Garage, Pottery, Oil Rig Worker O/P) **Geography:** 35 Titles: Arab Village, Boy in Bangladesh, Eskimo Boy, etc.		

Title and Publisher	PHASE*	INTEREST AGE	Reading Level A 5^{0}-5^{5}	B 5^{6}-5^{11}	C 6^{0}-6^{5}	D 6^{6}-6^{11}
B						
Beauties (O/P) Hart-Davis	P/S	8 - 11				
Be A Super Sleuth (Pied Piper Books) (O/P) Methuen	P/S	10 - 15				
Begin Here Oxford University Press	P/S	11 - 16				
Bestsellers (O/P) Murray	S	13 - 16				
Betty Root's Nature Stories Ginn	P	6 - 10				Honey Bee, Orange Tip Butterfly, Garden Spider, Emperor Dragonfly,
Book Bus Collins *(Each Phase is divided up into numbered packs. NASEN's grades should be regarded only as a rough guide.)* (T, S, AU, V, RR)	P	4 - 7	**Emergent Phase** Emergent A1 - (9 titles) ← Emergent B1 (14 titles) Emergent B2 (10 titles) Emergent C1 (10 titles) Emergent C2 (8 titles) Emergent C3 (11 titles) → (A–B) **Early Phase** ← Early A1 (8 titles) Early A2 (8 titles) Early A3 (5 titles) Early A4 (8 titles) Early B1 (8 titles) Early B2 (7 titles) Early B3 (10 titles) Early C1 (9 titles) Early C2 (9 titles) Early C3 (9 titles) → (A–C)			
Book of Letters, The (HI-LO Books) LDA	P	7 - 8				
Bookshelf Puzzlers Longman	P/S	7 - 12				
Bookshelf 6 (O/P) Collins	P	5 - 8			← Magic Days, Fireworks, It's Magic, Old and New, Penny and Mike, Pets and People, → (C–D)	

<table>
<tr><th>E
7^0-7^5</th><th>F
7^6-7^{11}</th><th>G
8^0-8^5</th><th>H
8^6-8^{11}</th><th>I
9^0-9^5</th><th>J
9^6-9^{11}</th><th>K
10^0-10^5+</th></tr>
<tr><td rowspan="2">1. The Secret Wish,
2. Missing!</td><td>3. A Real Beauty,</td><td colspan="2">← 9. Pups!
10. Copper, →</td><td rowspan="2"></td><td rowspan="2"></td><td rowspan="2"></td></tr>
<tr><td colspan="2">← 5. Beauty and the Bus,
6. Beauty, Bess and Bottle,
7. The Man in the Mist,
8. Poached Eggs, →</td><td></td></tr>
<tr><td></td><td></td><td></td><td colspan="2">← 1. The Case of the Face at the Window,
2. The Case of the Stolen Paintings,
3. The Case of the Invisible Witness,
4. The Case of the Bank Hold-up,
5. The Case of the High-Rise Robbery,
6. The Case of the Midnight Chess Game →</td><td></td><td></td></tr>
<tr><td></td><td></td><td></td><td colspan="3">1 title
Extracts, presenting a complete incident, from several well-known books
eg. Gumble's Yard, Stig of the Dump, The Silver Sword,</td><td></td></tr>
<tr><td colspan="2">30 titles including:
← Gypsy, Dream of the Dead, The Time Trap, →
Three Mile House, etc.</td><td></td><td></td><td></td><td></td><td></td></tr>
<tr><td></td><td></td><td></td><td></td><td></td><td></td><td></td></tr>
<tr><td></td><td></td><td></td><td></td><td></td><td></td><td></td></tr>
<tr><td></td><td colspan="2">← 1 title →</td><td></td><td></td><td></td><td></td></tr>
<tr><td></td><td></td><td></td><td></td><td>Level 1</td><td>Level 2, 3, 4</td><td>Level 5</td></tr>
<tr><td></td><td></td><td></td><td></td><td></td><td></td><td></td></tr>
</table>

B

Title and Publisher	PHASE*	INTEREST AGE	Reading Level A 5^0-5^5	B 5^6-5^{11}	C 6^0-6^5	D 6^6-6^{11}
Bookshelf (Harcourt, Brace) AMS Educational	P	7 - 10			**Stage 1** Breathing, Helping, Five Little Monkeys, Tails, **Stage 2** Whose Toes and Nose are Those?	Funny Talk and More, Going Shopping, Hands, Growing Radishes and Carrots, Melting, My Grandpa, Our Car, Oh Bother!, Chickens, Lorries, When Goldilocks Went to the House of the Bears, I Love Cats, The Old Man's Mitten, When the King Rides By, Where Does the Wind Go? **Stage 3** A Cat's Eye is One,
Breakthrough to Literacy Longman *(Reading books O/P. Main language experience materials still available.)*	P	5 - 9 *and older for green books*		← **Yellow A** After School, Big and Little, The Cat, The Bird and the Tree, The Fish Book, **Yellow B** At School, A Rainy Day, My Teacher, The Wendy House, **Yellow C** My Mum, I Fell Over, A Cup of Tea, Things I Can Do, **Yellow D** Looking After Baby, Eating, The Dog's Dream, Reading, **Yellow E** Buttons and Bows, Helping, Writing, A Fairy Story, **Yellow F** My Little Sister, My Dad, All Round the Year, When I Go to School, →		**Red A** Dressing Up, The Birthday Party, Doctors and Nurses, The Loose Tooth, **Red B** In Bed, Birds, The Christmas Tree, Shopping, **Red C** The Lost Girl, My Story, People in Stories, Our Baby, **Red D** A Home-made Mouse, My Cat, Monday's Child, How Would You Like It? **Red E** Butterflies, Colours, In the Giant's Shoe, Night and Morning,
Buccaneers/New Buccaneers Nelson	P/S	9 - 14				

E 7⁰-7⁵	F 7⁶-7¹¹	G 8⁰-8⁵	H 8⁶-8¹¹	I 9⁰-9⁵	J 9⁶-9¹¹	K 10⁰-10⁵+
Interruptions, Zoo-looking,	Caterpillars,					
A Bedtime Story, And Billy Went Out to Play, Floating and Sinking, How to Cook Scones, I Can Do It, One Hot Summer Night,	A Giant's Cake, The Greedy Goat, Everyone Knows About Cars,	It Didn't Frighten Me, Silly Billy,			Hospitals,	
Going Barefoot, Hiccups, Off To Squintum's, The Funny Old Man…, Up The Haystack, We're Off to Thunder Mountain,		Chicken in the Middle of the Road, Fishing for Beginners, Six Things to Make, The Old Woman Who Lived in a Vinegar Bottle, The Straight Line Wonder, Under a Stone, What Shall I Take?,	Dad's Diet, Tilly Tomkins Surprise Hat,	An International Airport, The Platypus,		
		Stage 4 The Frog Who Would Be King, The Nearly Always Come Again Hat, George the Giraffe,	Monster for Hire, The Breakfast Bird, The Dream Machine, What Makes A Bird A Bird?,	The Animal Joke Book, Six Red Hats,	An Introduction to Frogs, Look Up in the Sky, Lucky, No Strings Puppet Theatre Presents, Pheasant and Kingfisher,	And Now for the Weather, Folk Tales from Asia, King Joe of Bogpeat Castle, Things to Do When You're Bored,
Green A The Bike, The Canal, The Japanese Garden, The Paper Round,	**Green D** The Bridesmaid, In Hospital, My Island, Going to London,					
Green B The Swimming Bath, Mending a Puncture, The Record Player, My Friend's Country,	**Blue B** Fire!,					
Green C The Old Days, Making Life Easy, Do It Yourself, A Game,	**Blue C** Spider Webs, The Sun, The Moon, The Buttonhole,					
Blue A Crocodiles are Dangerous, Tom's Accident, Old Houses, Getting Married,	**Red F** Shirley Sharpeyes, Charlie Strong and his Favourite Song,					
Blue B The Football Match, The Day We Went to the Seaside, The New Flats,	**Red G** Signs, Hamlet the Hamster, Going to the Pictures, Whatever Next?,					
Red F Who's Scared? An Elephant in a Rhubarb Tree,						
				Set 1: Buccaneers 1. The Silver Ship, 2. The Island of Solomon Dee, 3. The Mystery of the Blue Whale, 4. The Journey Through the Strange Land, 5. The Fight for Ramir, 6. The Stolen Treasure, ← 7. Captain Rasha, → 8. The Island of Fire, **Set 2: New Buccaneers** Attack by Night! Captain Rasha, Shipwreck!, The Crown of Ramir, The Scarlet Berries…, The Rightful King of Ramir, The Sea-King's Treasure, Captain James…,	(spanned by arrow from I)	

Title and Publisher	PHASE*	INTEREST AGE	Reading Level A 5^{0}-5^{5}	B 5^{6}-5^{11}	C 6^{0}-6^{5}	D 6^{6}-6^{11}
B						
Bulls-eye Books (some titles O/P) Stanley Thornes	S	14 - 18+				
C						
Cambridge Reading Cambridge University Press	P	4 - 7	**Phase 1 - Beginning to Read** **Stage A** - 15 titles **Phase 2 - Becoming a Reader**	**Stage B** - 15 titles **Stage A** Contemporary - 3 titles Fantasy - 3 titles Traditional - 3 titles Childhood - 3 titles	← Poetry and Rhyme 3 titles →	**Phase 3 - Towards Independence**
Carry on Reading Schofield and Sims *[to be discontinued as stocks are exhausted]*	P	8 - 11				

<table>
<tr><th></th><th>E
7^{0}-7^{5}</th><th>F
7^{6}-7^{11}</th><th>G
8^{0}-8^{5}</th><th>H
8^{6}-8^{11}</th><th>I
9^{0}-9^{5}</th><th>J
9^{6}-9^{11}</th><th>K
10^{0}-10^{5}+</th></tr>
<tr><td rowspan="4">**B**</td><td></td><td></td><td>Jaws,
Casino Royale,
Goldfinger,
If Only They Could Talk,
Winged Escort,
Madam Will You Talk?,
Vets Might Fly,</td><td>The Triffids,
A Kind of Loving,
The Deep,
The Scorpio Letters, O/P
The Spy Who Came in from the Cold,
The Long Goodbye,
Dr. No,
Live and Let Die, O/P
Slay Ride, O/P</td><td>The Great Escape,
The Man with the Golden Gun,
On Her Majesty's Secret Service,</td><td>The Dam Busters,
The Devil's Alternative,</td><td>The Day of the Jackal,</td></tr>
<tr><td></td><td></td><td></td><td></td><td></td><td colspan="2">Ring of Bright Water,</td></tr>
<tr><td></td><td></td><td></td><td></td><td colspan="2">Diamonds Are For Ever,
The Loneliness of the Long Distance Runner, O/P</td><td></td></tr>
<tr><td></td><td></td><td></td><td colspan="2">Modesty Blaise,
A River Ran Out of Eden,
Walkabout,
It Shouldn't Happen to a Vet,
My Brother Michael,
Shout at the Devil,
Dracula,
The Chrysalids,
Frankenstein,</td><td></td><td></td></tr>
<tr><td rowspan="9">**C**</td><td colspan="2">Information Books</td><td></td><td></td><td></td><td></td><td></td></tr>
<tr><td>Osprey
Seals
Stage B
Contemporary - 3 titles
Fantasy - 3 titles
Traditional - 3 titles
Childhood - 3 titles</td><td>Dinosaurs

Poetry and Rhyme
- 3 titles</td><td></td><td>Information Books
- 3 titles</td><td></td><td></td><td></td></tr>
<tr><td colspan="2">**Stage C**
Contemporary - 3 titles
Fantasy - 3 titles
Traditional - 3 titles
Childhood - 3 titles
Poetry and Rhyme - 3 titles</td><td colspan="3">Information Books</td><td></td><td></td></tr>
<tr><td></td><td></td><td>The Scots Pine</td><td colspan="2">Animal Senses
Bubbles</td><td></td><td></td></tr>
<tr><td></td><td>Cutting and Sticking,
Parrot Talk,
Strawberry Picking,
Dad's Promise,
Tulips for Dad,
In the Mirror,</td><td>**Stage A**
The Big Shrink,
The Treasure Cave,
Dancing to the River,
Nonsense,</td><td>The Grabbing Bird,
How the Animals Got Their Tails,
Rabbit's Tail,
Ben's Amazing Birthday,
Marvel Paws,</td><td></td><td></td><td></td></tr>
<tr><td></td><td>The Dog Show,
The Pyjama Party,
The Special Cake,
The Haystack,</td><td>Jumble Power,
The Weather Drum,
A Welsh Lamb,</td><td>**Stage B**
The Peace King,
Volcano Women,
The Lord Mount Dragon,
Dancing in Soot,
Knicker-bocker Number Nine,</td><td>The Magic Sword,
A Corner of Magic,
A Lick of the Spoon,</td><td></td><td></td></tr>
<tr><td></td><td></td><td>A Cat for Keeps,
Don't be Late,
Spike and the Concert,
The Amazing Mr. Mulch,
The Slippery Planet,
Coyote Girl,</td><td>**Stage C**
Mr. Mulch's Magic Mixtures,</td><td>The Cape of Rushes,</td><td>The Most Beautiful Child,
A Shoot of Corn,
Snow in the Kitchen,
The Watch by the Sea,
Welcome Night,</td><td>A Mosquito in the Cabin,
Out and About,</td></tr>
<tr><td></td><td></td><td colspan="2">Red Book 1</td><td colspan="2">Red Book 3</td><td></td></tr>
<tr><td></td><td></td><td></td><td colspan="2">Red Book 2</td><td colspan="2">Red Book 4</td></tr>
<tr><td></td><td></td><td></td><td></td><td colspan="2">Blue Book 1</td><td colspan="2">Blue Book 3</td></tr>
<tr><td></td><td></td><td></td><td></td><td></td><td colspan="2">Blue Book 2</td><td>Blue 4</td></tr>
<tr><td></td><td></td><td></td><td></td><td></td><td></td><td>L
10^{6}-10^{11}</td><td>M
11^{0}-11^{5}+</td></tr>
<tr><td></td><td></td><td></td><td></td><td></td><td></td><td>Carry on Reading
Red Book 5</td><td>Red Book 6</td></tr>
<tr><td></td><td></td><td></td><td></td><td></td><td></td><td colspan="2">Blue Book 5</td></tr>
<tr><td></td><td></td><td></td><td></td><td></td><td></td><td></td><td>Blue 6</td></tr>
</table>

C

Title and Publisher	PHASE*	INTEREST AGE	Reading Level A 5^0-5^5	B 5^6-5^{11}	C 6^0-6^5	D 6^6-6^{11}
Castle of Grom Trilogy, The (HI-LO Books) LDA	P/S	9 - 16				
Cat on the Mat Books (O/P) Oxford University Press	P	4 - 6	Picture Books & Whose Shoes? The Apple Bird, The Nest, The Trunk, The Arrow, Dig Dig, The Island, Cat on the Mat, All Fall Down, Toot Toot, A Dog Called Mischief, Bump Bump, Frog and the Fly,	What a Tale, My Dream, My House, A Bag of Tricks,	Giddy Up, If I Were You, Tom and His Tractor, Sam's Big Day,	
Celebrations (O/P) Ginn	P/S	9 - 13+				
Changing Earth, The Ginn	P	4 - 6				
Children's Classics (Series 740) Ladybird	P/S	8 - 14				
City Links (Blackie) Nelson	P	7 - 11				
Cliffhangers Longman	P/S	8 - 13				
Close-up Books (O/P) Ginn	P/S	10 - 14				
Collins English Library Collins	P/S	10 - 16+				
Colour Jets A and C Black	P	6 - 10				
Comets Collins Educational	S	12 - 16				

E 7^{0}-7^{5}	F 7^{6}-7^{11}	G 8^{0}-8^{5}	H 8^{6}-8^{11}	I 9^{0}-9^{5}	J 9^{6}-9^{11}	K 10^{0}-10^{5}+
			← 3 Books →			
			← Divali, Christmas, Hanukka, Eid-ul-Fitry, Chinese New Year, Carnival, →			
		← Caves and Passages, Beaches and Coasts, Ice and Glaciers, Rivers and Valleys, Highlands and Lowlands, Volcanoes and Earthquakes, →				
		← 30 titles: A Tale of Two Cities, Treasure Island, The Railway Children, The Invisible Man, What Katy Did, Tom Sawyer, The Happy Prince, Gulliver's Travels, Heidi, The Lost World, King Solomon's Mines, etc. →				
	Kauser at Home, Shakoor is Born, The Good Luck Rakhi,	Praying with Ammi, Going to Mosque School, Ramadan and Eid-ul-Fitr, To the Temple for Arts, Dada Maa Dies, The Holi Fire,	Papa Ji Has Chickenpox, The Lights of Diwali,	A Happy Time at Eid-ul-Adha,		
				← Books 1, 2, 3 and 4 →		
					← Mountains and Moorland, Woodland and Forest, Meadows and Pasture, Rivers and Ponds, →	
	← Level 1: 20 titles Inspector Holt and The Fur Van, Where is Bill Ojo?, etc. →	← Level 2: 22 titles Inspector Holt Gets His Man, Muhammad Ali, etc. →		← Level 3: 22 titles Brainbox and Ball, Cinema Stunts, etc. →	← Level 4: 18 titles King Solomon's Mines, Landslide, etc. → **L 10^{6}-10^{11}** Level 5: 14 titles The Guns of Navarone, Geordie	**N 11^{6}-11^{0}** Level 6: 10 titles Doctor Zhivago, The Glory Boys, etc.
		← Dad on the Run Even Stevens FC, Francis Fry, Private Eye, Stinker Muggles and the Dazzle Bug, →				
		← **Pack 2** No More Heroes, The Great Safe Blag, Beware the Elvis Man, Time Exchange, Exterminators 2: Humans 0, Exterminators, The Tornado, →				

C

Title and Publisher	PHASE*	INTEREST AGE	Reading Level A 5^0-5^5	B 5^6-5^{11}	C 6^0-6^5	D 6^6-6^{11}
Compact Classics Ward Lock	P/S	11 - 15+				
Connections (O/P) Ginn	P/S	5 - 12	**Discussion Books** 1. Colour Journey, 2. Colours, 3. Where We Live, 4. Hunt the Tiger, 5. Photo Album, 6. Animals, **Story Books** 1. It Must be Red, Painting the Fence, Chameleon, Follow Me, 2. Jungle Crazy, Ice Cream, Look at This, My New Jumper, 3. House for Sale, Come to a Party, The Dog House, Making a House, 4. I Like My House, My New House, My House Has Wheels, My House, 5. I Like..., Good Night, I Walked to School, Friends, 6. Boo!, My Dog, What's in the Box?, Lost Dog, *[**Note:** The Discussion Books relate closely to the Story Books as indicated by the editor's numbering, above.]*	1. Class Photo, 2. Bigger than a Mouse, 3. The Supermarket, 4. My Favourite Things, 1. Happy Birthday, My Baby Sister, Come to Tea, Potters, 2. Be a Cat, Pets, Animals, If..., 3. Good Food, Apples and Pears, Lots on Top, Vegetable Soup, 4. Camping, Walking Home, Shopping, I Like Rubbish,		
Contact Readers (O/P) Collins	S	12 - 16				
Crown Reading Programme Nelson	P/S	8 - 13	**(Stage 1)** **Mainline** 1. We Live in the Castle, 2. The Castle is Old..., 3. We Mend the Castle, Workbook 1 **Supplementary** 3a. The Cook and the Cakes, 3b. The Maid and the Mouse, 3c. The Coachman, Workbook 2		**(Stage 2)** 4. We Paint the Castle, 5. We Make a Garden, 6. We Have a Garden Party, Workbook 3 6a. The Baby's New Clothes, 6b. The Little Guard's Birthday, 6c. The King's Boat, Workbook 4	**(Stage 3)** 7. No Egg for the King, 8. Kite Flying Day, 9. The Sausage Machine, 9a. The Pram Race, 9b. A Baby and a Snowman, 9c. The Maid Wins a Prize, Phonic Workbook

D

Title and Publisher	PHASE*	INTEREST AGE	Reading Level A 5^0-5^5	B 5^6-5^{11}	C 6^0-6^5	D 6^6-6^{11}
Dan Frontier Books (O/P) Harcourt Brace	P/S	7 - 14				Dan Frontier and the New House, Dan Frontier and the Big Cat, Dan Frontier Goes Hunting,
Databank Series (Some titles O/P) Hodder and Stoughton	S	11 - 16				

	E 7^0-7^5	F 7^6-7^{11}	G 8^0-8^5	H 8^6-8^{11}	I 9^0-9^5	J 9^6-9^{11}	K 10^0-10^5+
C					← **Level 1** The Adventures of Huckleberry Finn, King Solomon's Mines, The Adventures of Don Quixote, Swiss Family Robinson, The Prisoner of Zenda, The Adventures of Tom Sawyer, Around the World in 80 Days, Little Women, David Copperfield, Oliver Twist, Silas Marner, The Coral Island, Robinson Crusoe, →		**Level 2** Great Expectations, Pride and Prejudice, Jane Eyre, Ivanhoe, Kidnapped, Treasure Island, The Three Musketeers, Tales from Shakespeare, More Tales from Shakespeare, Emma, Wuthering Heights, Vanity Fair, Rebecca, A Tale of Two Cities,
				← **Level 9** Firelight, Against the Odds, Anyone at Home, Helping Hands, → ← **Level 10** Water Water Everywhere, Strange Truth Strange Fiction, The Long Walk, Making Your Mark, →	← **Level 11** For When We Dream, Friends and Enemies, What on Earth? Over and Out, →	← **Level 12** Visions and Voices, Give Me a Clue, Airways, Living with Animals, →	
			← **First Contact:** 4 titles 1. Go and Find Him, 2. River of Danger 3. The Great Bed Race, 4. Night Raid (+ workbooks) → ← **Contact:** 8 titles Last Across, The Match, Dead of Night, Road Race, A Hard Man, Catch, Day in the Country, The Long Drop, →				
	(Stage 4) 10. Hugo the Magician, 11. The Pink Ghost, 12. The Broomstick Tree, 12a. The Dragons…, 12b. The Giant and the Blue Castle, 12c. The Robbers and the Red Queen,						
D	Dan Frontier Trapper, Dan Frontier with the Indians, ← Dan Frontier and the Wagon Train, Dan Frontier Scouts with the Army, →	← Dan Frontier Sheriff, Dan Frontier Goes Exploring, →		Dan Frontier Goes to Congress,			
					30 titles: Canals, Castles, Manors, Monasteries, Railways, Roads, Sound, Light, Heat, Deserts, Money, Parliament, Newspapers, Food, Dinosaurs, The Anglo-Saxons, The Celts, The Romans, The Greeks,		

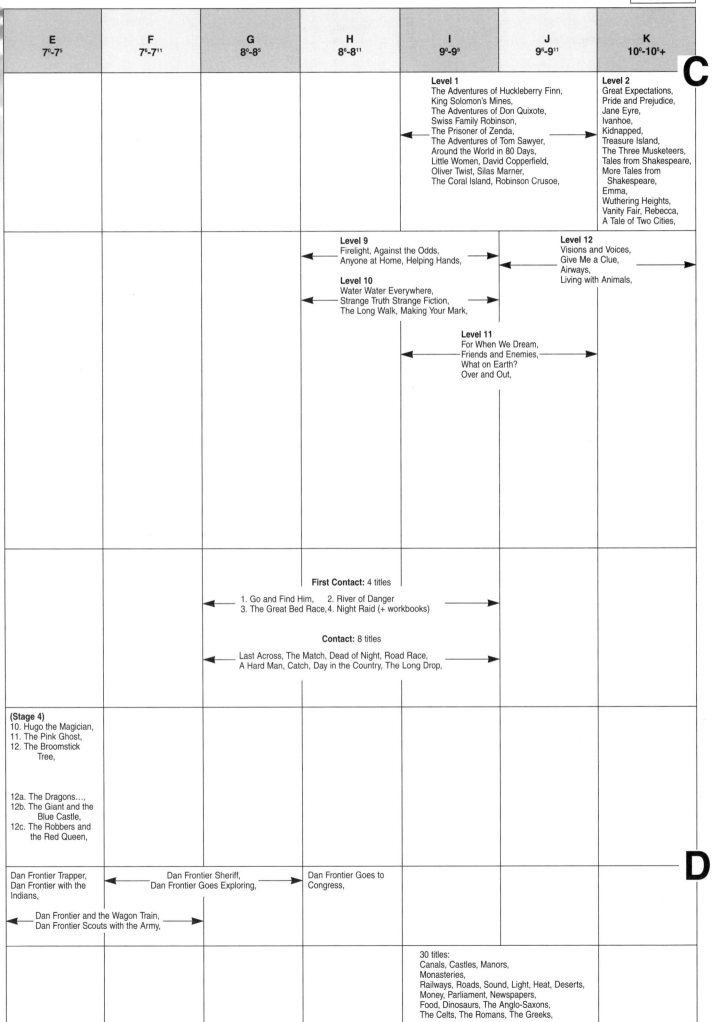

Title and Publisher	PHASE*	INTEREST AGE	Reading Level A 5^0-5^5	B 5^6-5^{11}	C 6^0-6^5	D 6^6-6^{11}
D						
Datasearch Hodder and Stoughton	S	11 - 16				
Day-to-Day Readers Basic Skills Agency	S	11 - adult				**Series A** The Accident,
Deckford Five, The (O/P) Simon and Schuster	P/S	11 - 15				
Discover (O/P) Simon and Schuster	P	6 - 10				
Discovering Together (O/P) Harcourt Brace	P	6 - 7				Christmas, At the Shops,
Dog Tales Ginn	P	6 - 9				
Don't Do That! (O/P) Ginn	P	6 - 8+			Don't Do That! The Green Monkey, In My House, I Am a Ghost, The Birthday Party, The Spaceship,	
Duncan Dragon Readers (O/P) Harcourt Brace	P	5 - 8	1, 2, 3 and 4 4a, 4b, 4c	5, 6	7, 8 ← 8a, 8b, 8c →	9, 10 10a, 10b, 10c
E						
Eagle Books (O/P) Oxford University Press	P/S	9 - 13				
Easy Reader Adventure Stories (O/P) LDA	P/S	11 - 14				
Easy Reading Bible Stories (Series 606A) Ladybird (Series 8610)	P	6 - 9				

	E 7^0-7^5	F 7^6-7^{11}	G 8^0-8^5	H 8^6-8^{11}	I 9^0-9^5	J 9^6-9^{11}	K 10^0-10^5+
D							Air and Breathing, Heating and Cooling, Sound and Hearing, Light and Seeing,
	Series A Lonely Hearts, A New Man, A Friend in Need,	**Series B** The Victim, Long Time No See, Run Away, Red Handed,	**Series C** You Win Some, The Baby, Crash, A New Life,				
				The Rescue, Bad Dreams, The Runaway, Guitar, The Party, Guitar Man, All the Fun of the Fair,			
		Spring Days on the Farm,	A Shepherd's Year, Behind the Scenes, ← Sea Turtles Hatching,	→			
	Pets, Weather						
			Thingummyrobert, Tiny, Sally, Anna, Duckling, Joe,				
	11, 12 12a, 12b, 12c	13 ← 14a, 14b, 14c	14 →				
E			← Little Angel Comes to Stay, Junk Castle, My Uncle Had Nothing to Do with It, Little Angel Bonjour,	→	Glubbslyme, Anastasia Morningstar,		
				← Twin and Super Twin, The Demon Headmaster, The Prime Minister's Brain, Forgett's Revenge, Gone to the Dogs, Jump!		→	
				← Three Books		→	
	Series 606A: Jesus the Friend, The Baby Jesus, Children of the Bible (O/P), Jesus the Helper, The Sower, The Lost Sheep (O/P), The Loaves and Fishes (O/P), The Good Samaritan (O/P),	Water into Wine (O/P), Two New House (O/P), **Series 8610:** When God Made Adam and Eve, Noah, Abraham, Jacob,					

E

Title and Publisher	PHASE*	INTEREST AGE	Reading Level A 5^0-5^5	B 5^6-5^{11}	C 6^0-6^5	D 6^6-6^{11}
Easy Readers (O/P) Murray	S	11 - 18				
Easystarts Longman	P/S	10 - 14				←
Echoes (O/P) Macmillan	P/S	8 - 12				
Encounter Books (O/P) Cassell	S	13 - 18+				
Energy (O/P) Ginn	P/S	8 - 12				
English Headwork, Headwork Stories Oxford University Press *[also see Primary Headwork and Headwork Reading]*	S	11 - 15				
English Picture Readers (O/P) Oxford University Press	P/S	9 - 16				
Environment Books (O/P) Macmillan	P/S	10 - 15				
Evidence in History (Simon and Schuster) Stanley Thornes	P/S	10 - 15				
Explore a Story (O/P) Collins	P/S	9 - 13				

E 7^{0}-7^{5}	F 7^{6}-7^{11}	G 8^{0}-8^{5}	H 8^{6}-8^{11}	I 9^{0}-9^{5}	J 9^{6}-9^{11}	K 10^{0}-10^{5}+
		The Speckled Band, The Champawat Man-Eater,	← The Way Up to Heaven, The Hound of the Baskervilles, Dr. Jekyll and Mr. Hyde, →	← Black Peter, Treasure Island, →		
24 titles including: Dino's Day in London, Flying Home, The Last Photo, Maisie and the Dolphin, Tinker's Island, Who Wants to be a Star? →						
What happened… 1. to Sam, 2. in the Park, 3. in the Hills, 5. at 9 o'clock, 6. at Breakfast,	7. in School, 8. on the No. 12 Bus, 9. to Sam's Grandad, 10. to Pam's Song, 11. at the Match, 12. in Space,					
					← 11 titles: Flop and Mick, Under the Silkwood, Black Lake, Red Snapper Night, Shadows, etc. →	
			← What is Energy?, Moving Around, Energy at Home, Energy at Work, Where Does Energy Come From, Making the Most of Energy, →			
			Book 1	Book 2 ← Headwork Stories 1 →	Book 3	Book 4 Headwork Stories 2
← **Grade 1: World's Greatest Stories** 13 titles: Sinbad the Sailor, Aladdin and Ali Baba, King Arthur and His Knights, Don Quixote, etc. →		← **Grade 2: Pictorial Classics** 8 titles: Around the World in Eighty Days, Kidnapped, Robinson Crusoe, Lorna Doone, etc. →				
						On a Farm, By Land, Sea and Air, Under Your Feet, On Holiday, Dial 999, In Town, Back in the Past, Made in Britain,
						Early Civilization, Prehistoric Britain, The Greek and Roman World, The Romans, The Vikings, The Saxons, The Normans, The Middle Ages, The Tudors, The Stuarts, Developing Britain, Government and People, Twentieth Century Britain, The Twentieth Century World,
		Pack 1: 3 titles Toussaint L'ouverture Ann Hurst, Three Folk Tales, Pack 2: 3 titles Spartacus, Three Folk Tales, Marcus Garrey,	← Pack 3: 3 titles Lin Tse Hsu, James the African Prince, Three Folk Stories, → ← Pack 4: 3 titles Olaudah Equiano, Te Whiti, Rani of Jhansi, →			

Title and Publisher	PHASE*	INTEREST AGE	Reading Level A 5^{0}-5^{5}	B 5^{6}-5^{11}	C 6^{0}-6^{5}	D 6^{6}-6^{11}
E						
Exploring Religion Collins	P/S	10 - 14				
F						
Fables (Series 742) Ladybird						
Fables from Aesop Ginn	P	5 - 7			1-6 The Goose that Laid the Golden Eggs, The Ass in the Lion's Skin, The Fox and the Crow, The Boy Who Cried Wolf, The Boy and the Lion, Town Mouse and Country Mouse,	7-12 The Ducks and the Tortoise, The Eagle and the Man, The Ass in the Pond, The Man, His Son and their Ass, The Donkey and the Lap Dog, The Farmer and his Sons,
Fastbacks (HI-LO Books) LDA	P/S	10 - 16				
Favourite Fairy Tales (O/P) Longman	P	7 - 10				
Feasts and Seasons (O/P) Nelson	P/S	9 - 13				
Festival Books (O/P) Nelson	P/S	8 - 12				
First Look At..., A (O/P) Watts	P/S	8 - 14				
First Nature Books (O/P) Black	P	6 - 9				
First Nature Watch Ginn	P	5 - 7	Books 1-12: The Bluetit, The Cat, The Cherry Tree, The Dandelion, etc. Books 13-18: The Arctic Fox, The Hen, The Polar Bear, The Tree, The Hamster, The Butterfly,			
First Sight (O/P) A and C Black	P	6 - 10				

E 7^0-7^5	F 7^6-7^{11}	G 8^0-8^5	H 8^6-8^{11}	I 9^0-9^5	J 9^6-9^{11}	K 10^0-10^5+
					← Festivals, Writings, Worship, Signs and Symbols, Buildings, People, →	
Aesop's Fables (Book 1)	Aesop's Fables (Book 2)					
13-18 The Hare and the Tortoise, The Fox and the Stork, The Lion and the Mouse, The Bear and the Travellers, The Sick Lion, The Monkey and the Fisherman, →						
	Horror Stories, The Caller, Guts, Live Bait, Mad Dog,	**Romance Stories** Survival Camp, Maggie, Just Like Everyone Else, Oh, Rick!	**Mystery Stories** A Game for Fools, Bill Waite's Will, Cardiac Arrest, The Intruder,			
	The Ugly Duckling, etc. (6 titles)					
						Spring, Summer, Autumn, Winter,
				Diwali,		Ramadan and Eid-ul-Fitr, Carnival, Chinese New Year,
				← 29 titles: Airports, Arms and Armour, Cars, Castles, Cats, Comets, Computers, BMX Bikes, Dinosaurs, Dogs, Earthquakes, Fossils, The Moon, Robots, Seasons, Trees, Weather, Submarines, Space Shuttle, etc. →		
	← The Fly, The Ladybird, The Grasshopper, The Snail, The Mushroom, →					
← Dinosaur Bones, Germs Make Me Sick! Get Ready for Robots!, Rock Collecting, Snow is Falling, What Makes Day and Night, Evolution, →						

F

Title and Publisher	PHASE*	INTEREST AGE	Reading Level A 5^0-5^5	B 5^6-5^{11}	C 6^0-6^5	D 6^6-6^{11}
Five Minute Thrillers (HI-LO Books) LDA (AU)	P/S	10 - 16				
Flamingo Books (O/P) Oliver and Boyd	P	8 - 11				**Pink 1:** 4 titles Matilda, etc.
Flightpath to Reading Nelson *[See Tim Books Pub. by Nelson p100]*	P/S	9 - 14				
Flying Boot Nelson (T, S, IT, RR)	P	4 - 6	**Stage 1** **Stories** - (12 books), **Environmental Print:** Max in Town, **Non-Fiction:** Max's Boot of Boots and Shoes, Max's Book of Flying, **Stage 2** **Stories** - (12 books), **Environmental Print:** Where is Ruff? **Non-Fiction:** Max's Book of the Body, Max's Book of Families,	**Stage 3** **Stories** - (12 books), **Environmental Print:** No Dogs, **Non-Fiction:** Max's Book of Friends, Max's Book of Shops, ← **Stage 4** **Stories** - (12 books), →	**Stage 5** **Stories** - (12 books),	**Environmental Print:** Our School, **Non-Fiction:** Max's Book of Recycling, Max's Book of the City of London, **Environmental Print:** A Day Out, **Non-Fiction:** Max's Book of Magnets, Max's Book of the Village of Dent,
Flying Carpets (O/P) Macmillan	P	7 - 10				
Focus on Sport Learning Materials Ltd.	P/S	10 - 14				
Focus Stories (O/P) Oliver and Boyd	P/S	10 - 13				
Food Wayland	P/S	9 - 15				
Foundations for Life Hodder and Stoughton	S	14 - 16				

E 7^{0}-7^{5}	F 7^{6}-7^{11}	G 8^{0}-8^{5}	H 8^{6}-8^{11}	I 9^{0}-9^{5}	J 9^{6}-9^{11}	K 10^{0}-10^{5}+
← **Set 1:** 16 titles including: The Arsonist, The Look-Alike, The Everett Eyes, The Playmate, Someone at the Door, Princess, Flight 901, The Hitchhiker, etc. → ← **Set 2:** A Time to Remember, The Specialist, The Blue Club, Chan, A Matter of Time, The Birthday Present, Friday Afternoon, The Costume Party, →						
Red 1: 4 titles The Fish and Chip Man, etc. **Pink 2:** 4 titles The Three Balloons, etc.	← **Red 2:** 4 titles The Fisher Boy, etc. → **Pink 3:** 4 titles The Street of Steps, etc.		**Red 3:** 4 titles The Village that Was Drowned, etc. ← **Pink 4:** 4 titles The Wooden Dog, etc. →	**Red 4:** 4 titles The Anonios Alone, etc.		
	← **Set A:** 8 titles →	← **Set B:** 8 titles →	← **Set C:** 8 titles → ← **Set D:** 8 titles →			
			← A Small Pudding for Wee Gowrie, The Boy Who Turned into a Goat, Beyond the Firelight, The Worm and the Toffee-Nosed Princess, Fog Hounds, Wind Cat, Sea Mice, The Little Master of the Elephant, →			
			Focus on Sport, 1 title			
		← Book 1 →		← Book 2 →		
			← 20 titles including: Apples, Cheese, Chocolate, Beans and Pulses, Bread, Butter, Citrus Fruit, Eggs, Fish, Meat, Milk, Pasta, Potatoes, Rice, Sugar, Vegetables, Coffee, Tea, Herbs and Spices, etc. →			
			You and Your Community			Work and Leisure, Home, Family and Health,

Title and Publisher	PHASE*	INTEREST AGE	Reading Level A 5^{0}-5^{5}	B 5^{6}-5^{11}	C 6^{0}-6^{5}	D 6^{6}-6^{11}
F						
Francie Stories Ginn	P	6 - 8+				Francie and the Joke Tellers,
Fuzzbuzz Oxford University Press (T, S, IT)	P/S	8 - 14	**Level 1:** Yellow 1. The Black Box, 2. The Fuzzbuzz, ← **Words 1** →	3. The Garden, 4. The Dump, **Level 1A:** 6.1 The Big House, 6.2 Eggin and His Playthings, 6.3 The Van, 6.4 The Buzzit, 6.5 Eggin and the Fuzzbuzzes, 6.6 The End of the Buzzit,	5. The Slinx, 6. The Trick, **Level 2:** Red 7. The Glen,	8. The Clan, 9. The Haggis Hunt, ← **Level 2A:** 12.1 The Slinx Has a Problem, 12.2 The Biggest Dump…,
G						
Galaxy 5 (O/P) Murray	P/S	10 - 15				
Giant, The (O/P) Ginn	P	6 - 8+				On Sunday the Giant, On Monday…, On Tuesday…, On Wednesday…, On Thursday…, On Friday…,
Good and Bad Cherrytree Press	P	7 - 11				
Graded Reading Series (O/P) Ward Lock	P/S	10 -15				**Level 1** Do All You Dare, Little Girl Lost, The Hunting Dog, Mike's Assignment, ←
Grasshopper Books (O/P) Penguin	P/S	8 - 13				
Great Unknown, The (O/P) Ginn	P	6 - 8		The Mountain, The Desert, The Ocean, The Jungle,		
Griffin Pirate Stories Nelson			*See Pirate Reading Scheme*			
Grobot Nisbet	P	6 - 9	1. Grobot the Robot,	2. Grobot and the Motor Mouse,	3. Grobot and the Animals,	4. Grobot on the Beach,

E 7^0-7^5	F 7^6-7^{11}	G 8^0-8^5	H 8^6-8^{11}	I 9^0-9^5	J 9^6-9^{11}	K 10^0-10^5+
Francie and the TV Play, Francie Come to My House,	Francie and the Birthday Party,					
10. Jock the Pocket, 11. Don the Bonnet, ← **Words 2** → (E–F) 12.3 The Rocket, 12.3 Zaxon,	12. The Contest, 12.5 The Honkbonk, 12.6 Going Back,	**Link:** Letters 1 and 2 ← **Level 3:** 13. The Trip, 14. The Glen of Gloom, 15. The Snagron, 16. The Wall, → (G–H)		17. The Prisoner 18. The Scouting Party, 19. The Getaway, 20. The Last Battle,		
6 titles: Goodbye to Earth, On the Red World, Vacation in Space, Dead Moon, Where No Sun Shines, King of the Stars,						
	Thief, Liar, Moody, Bully, Cheat, Selfish,					
Level 2 What Shall We Do With It? Accident; Tiger, Tiger!, The Big Star Day, **Level 3** (E–F) Good Save, Control to Baby One, Day Trip, F-I-S-H-Fish, →	← **Level 4** (F–G) Love at First Sight, The Day I Took the Bull by the Horns, That's How It Is, The Ghost Fish, →					
	← **Red titles:** (7) (F–G) The Princess and the Cat, School on the Moon, etc. →	← **Blue titles:** (11) (G–H) The Pine Street Pageant, Flight of Fancy, →	← **Green titles:** (7) (H–I) Albert's World Tour, Kilroy and the Gull, etc. →			

H

Title and Publisher	PHASE*	INTEREST AGE	Reading Level A 5^{0}-5^{5}	B 5^{6}-5^{11}	C 6^{0}-6^{5}	D 6^{6}-6^{11}
Hair Raisers Longman *[Each story in pictures, speech bubbles and full length.]*	S	12 - 16				
Handi-Read Books (O/P) LDA *[Life skills for children with severe learning difficulties.]*	P	8+				
Happy Families Penguin	P	7 - 11				
Happy Venture Longman *[All Library Books O/P]*	P	5 - 9	Approach book I Can Read Intro. book Fluff and Nip, Library books 1-5 Hide and Seek,	1. Playtime Playbook 1, Story Time, Library books 6-10 The Bad Kitten, etc.	2. Our Friends Playbook 2, Saturday Play, Library books 11-15 Little Chick's Shadow, etc.	3. Growing Up Playbook 3. Now for Some Stories, Library books 16-21 Sally's Kitchen, etc.
Harry Stories (O/P) Harcourt Brace	S	11 - 16				
Headlines (Edward Arnold) Hodder and Stoughton	S	12 - 16+				
Headwork Reading Oxford University Press	P/S	10 - 15				
Heinemann Guided Readers Heinemann	P/S	11 - 16				

E 7^0-7^5	F 7^6-7^{11}	G 8^0-8^5	H 8^6-8^{11}	I 9^0-9^5	J 9^6-9^{11}	K 10^0-10^5+
			← Sweeny Todd, Jack the Ripper, Burke and Hare, Dr. Jekyll and Mr. Hyde, →			
← Kate Goes by Bus, Jane Shops at the Supermarket, Jane Telephones her Friends, Andrew Goes to the Swimming Pool, →						
	Mr. Biff the Boxer, Mr. Cosmo the Conjurer, Mrs. Plug the Plumber, Miss Jump the Jockey, Mrs. Lather's Laundry, Mr. Tick the Teacher, Miss Brick the Builder's Baby, Mr. Buzz the Bee Man, Mr. and Mrs. Hag the Horse,	Mrs. Wobble the Waitress, Master Salt the Sailor's Son, Master Money the Millionaire,				
4. Holiday Time Playbook 4. Far and Wide, Library books 22-27 The Little Kangaroo, etc.	← **Leading to Wide Range Readers** →					
		1. Lucky Harry, 2. Harry Takes His Time,				
			← 1. Daredevils, 2. Survivors from the Sea, 3. Remarkable Animals, 4. Record Breakers, 5. Movie Monsters, 6. Unsolved Mysteries, 7. Spies, 8. Hoaxers and Swindlers, 9. Sporting Superstars, 10. Rescued! 11. Exploring Space, 12. Treasure, 13. Heroes and Heroines, 14. Disasters, 15. Ghosts, 16. Gangsters, (some O/P) →			
Headwork 1: A Pain in the Neck Nappy Attack, Rat's Revenge, The Ice Orcs, Strangers on the Shore, A Gift from Elsa, **Headwork 2:** A Bit of a Drip, Madman's Corner, Snake in a Bed, No One for Games, Paper Shop Hold-up, Goblin Ring, ← **Headwork 3:** Thanks But No Thanks, Money and Old Coats, Slow Motion, →	← **Headwork 4:** Aunt Jane's Attic, The Locked Room, Hot Dog, →					
Starter Level: 9 titles The Lost Ship, Alissa, Sara Says No! Blue Fins, The Briefcase, Ski Roll, etc.	← **Beginner Level:** 11 titles Anna and the Fighter, This London, This is Barcelona, The Sky's the Limit, plus remaining 7 titles. →			← **Elementary Level:** Road to Nowhere, The Black Cat, Don't Tell Me What To Do, The Red Pony, The Flower Seller, The Hound of the Baskervilles, etc. →		**L Intermediate Level 10^2-11^0** Shane, Old Mali and the Boy, A Man from Glasgow, Bristol Murder, The Enchanted April, No Comebacks, etc. **M Upper Level 11^0+** Of Mice and Men, The Money for Sale, The Grapes of Wrath, Bleak House, Rebecca, etc.

H

Title and Publisher	PHASE*	INTEREST AGE	Reading Level A 5^{0}-5^{5}	B 5^{6}-5^{11}	C 6^{0}-6^{5}	D 6^{6}-6^{11}
High Noon Books Ann Arbor Publishers	P/S	9 - 16				**Meg Parker Mysteries** - (6 books)
High Stakes Adventures (HI-LO Books) LDA	P/S	10 - 16				
Highways and Byways (O/P) Nelson	P/S	7 - 13				
Hill Street Gang, The Learning Materials Ltd.	P/S	10 - 16				Book 1
Hipsters Longman	S	12 - 16				
History of Britain (Series F895) Ladybird	P/S	8 - 14				
History of Britain (O/P) Macmillan	P/S	9 - 14				
Horror Classics (Series 841) (O/P) Ladybird	P/S	10 - 16				
How It Works (Series 654) (Some titles O/P) Ladybird	P/S	10 - 14+				
How We Used to Live A and C Black *(In association with Yorkshire TV)*	P/S	10 - 16				

E 7^0-7^5	F 7^6-7^{11}	G 8^0-8^5	H 8^6-8^{11}	I 9^0-9^5	J 9^6-9^{11}	K 10^0-10^5+
Tom and Ricky Mystery Series Sets 1-9 (6 books) in each set) **Scoop Doogan Series** Sets 1 and 2 (6 books in each set) **Road Aces Series** Sets 1 and 2 (6 books in each set) ← **Perspectives 1** - (10 books) → **Numero Uno Gang Mysteries** - (5 books) Mysterious Letters,	**Annie Wilkins Mystery Series** - (5 books) **Life Line Series** - (5 books) **High Adventures** ← Sets 1 and 2 - (5 books in each Set) → **High School Highways** ← Sets 1 and 2 - (5 books in each Set) → **Legal Eagle Series** The Treasure in the Well, The Borrowed Banker,	**Unusual Events** Flying Circus, Street of the Unknown Ghost, The Stolen Secrets, The Ghosts of Black Point,	Mystery of the Strange Creature, The Dubarry Diamond,			
		← The Little Ones, Race Against the River, Crash Landing, Jump, →	← Shocked to Death, Room-mate Wanted, Murder by Phone, Knife in the Dark, →			
			← **Just the Job:** 4 titles Animal Nurse, etc. → ← **One Hundred Years Ago:** 4 titles Shops and Street Traders, etc. →		← **Islands:** 4 titles Malta, etc. → ← **Bird Families:** 4 titles Finches, etc. →	
Book 2	Book 3	Book 4				
	← Go for Goal, Racing Bike, Snake Run, Hot Wheels, Hush-a-Bye Baby, Blow Up, Gate Crashers, The Bike, Out of the Dark, The Open Grave, The Forbidden Room, Accident, The Secret, Fire on the Sea, Digging for Treasure, Flood, The Sunday Papers, Sausages on the Shore, No Ladder for Tom Bates, High Jacks Low Jacks, First Day Out, Crash Car, Holiday House, Strong Arm, →					
		← The Romans, The Saxons and the Normans, The Middle Ages, The Tudors, (so far) →				
			← 1. Before 1066, 2. The Middle Ages, 3. Henry VII to George III, 4. Modern Times, →			
		← Dracula, The Mummy, Frankenstein, The Hound of the Baskervilles, Dr. Jekyll..., Ghostly Tales, (Series 872) →				
				← The Motor Car, The Rocket, The Aeroplane, Television, The Locomotive, The Hovercraft, The Camera, Farm Machinery, The Computer, The Telescopes, Printing Processes, The Telephone, (Some O/P) →		
			← How We Used to Live 1954-1970 How We Used to Live 1902-1926 →			

Title and Publisher	PHASE*	INTEREST AGE	Reading Level A 5^{0}-5^{5}	B 5^{6}-5^{11}	C 6^{0}-6^{5}	D 6^{6}-6^{11}
H						
Hummingbirds Collins	P/S	7 - 12				
I						
I Am Adopted Series Bodley Head	P	5 - 9				I Am Adopted, The House Where Jack Lives,
I Can Read (Mammoth)	P	6 - 7				
If I Could Be … (O/P) Ginn	P	5 - 7		If I Could Be a Frog, …a Lion, …a Seal, …a Chipmunk, …a Fish, …a Monkey,		
I Love Animals (O/P) Ginn	P	7 - 11				
Impact Ginn	P/S	10 - 14				
In My Class (O/P) Ginn (RR)	P	8 - 11				
Inside Story (O/P) Blackie	P	7 - 9				

E 7^0-7^5	F 7^6-7^{11}	G 8^0-8^5	H 8^6-8^{11}	I 9^0-9^5	J 9^6-9^{11}	K 10^0-10^5+
H						
	Early Group Miranda and the Magic Mixture, The Witch's Cat, The Golden Chain, The Purse Full of Gold, Adventures in the Night, The Story of Yestin, The Nobleman and the Dwarf,	**Group 2** Jacca and the Talking Dog, The Dancers from the Land of Mor, The Giant Owls of the Hills, Peter and the Little Fox, The Magic People, Witches in the Magic Wood,				
	Group 1 The Green Man and the Golden Bird, Mrs. Blue-hat is Very Cross, The Magic Cloak, The Horses of the Moonlight, Hallowe'en, Sharon and the Great Horse,		**Group 3** The Ivory Dragon, Lion-Men of the Mountains, The Great and Terrible Gift, The Rescue of Ker, The King with Four Daughters, The Dangerous Journey,			
I						
Ben, The Boy Who Couldn't Hear, Rachel,						
		Little Bear, Little Bear's Friend, A Kiss for Little Bear,	Father Comes Home,			
	Kitten, Hedgehog, Pony, Swan, Squirrel, Puppy,					
	Set A Double Take, Martin's Midnight Muddle, Sorry, Miss Brown, Diary of a Megahero,	Frank Bruno, Arnold Schwartzenegger,	Joke Book, **Set B** Hall End High 1, Hall End High 2, Hall End High 3, BzzzSplat! The Impact Poetry Book, Sophie's Secret Diary, Fishing, Motorcycling, **Set C** Crush, Love from Kary, Colin the Barbarian, The Pit,	Demons in Disguise, The Watersnake,		
The Birthday Party, Tom Gets Lost, Alone at Home, The Bullies,						
				The Police, The Post Office, The Fire Station, The Hospital, Water, Airports, Railways, Waste Disposal,		

Title and Publisher	PHASE*	INTEREST AGE	Reading Level A 5^{0}-5^{5}	B 5^{6}-5^{11}	C 6^{0}-6^{5}	D 6^{6}-6^{11}
I						
Insight Nelson *[A series about disabilities]*	P	7 - 11				
In the Picture (O/P) Simon and Schuster	P	7 - 11				
I See What You Mean Longman	P/S	10 - 13				
J						
Janet and John Nisbet	P	5 - 10	**Whole Word Series** Here We Go, **Phonic Series** Here We Go, My Little Books, 1-5, (O/P)	Off to Play, Book 1 My Little Books, 6-10, (O/P)	Out and About, My Little Books, 11-15, (some O/P)	I Went Walking, Book 2 My Little Books, 16-32, (some O/P)
Jets A and C Black	P	6 - 11				
Jim Hunter Books (O/P) Methuen	S	11 - 15				
Joe's Gang (O/P) Ginn	P	5 - 7+				Building a House, The Space Rocket, The Big Show, The Shop, Making a Monster, The Band,
Johnny Black Stories, The (O/P) Arnold-Wheaton	S	11 - 15				

E 7^0-7^5	F 7^6-7^{11}	G 8^0-8^5	H 8^6-8^{11}	I 9^0-9^5	J 9^6-9^{11}	K 10^0-10^5+
← **Series 1:** My Friend Lucy, My Cousin Dan, Dan My New Neighbour, Emma, My Friend Andrew, My Sister Sarah, **Series 2:** Peter, My Best Friend, Life Is Not So Sweet, My Father, David, Something Different in the Bank, →						
	Our Planet, Air, Water, Animals,					
						Books 1 & 2
Through the Garden Gate, Book 3, Blue Stories 13. Mr. Vinegar, 15. Little Red Riding Hood, Plum Stories 1-10	I Know a Story, Book 4 Pink Stories (7 in print) Lime Stories 1-10	Once Upon a Time, High on a Hill, Maroon Stories 31-38 Cherry Stories 1-10	Days in the Sun, The Five and a Half Club, Over the Sea, O/P It Must Be Magic,	Magic Everywhere, Brave and Bold, O/P		
	Mum's the Word, The Thing-on-two-legs, Sharon and Darren,	← Albertine, Goose Queen, Changing Charlie, Clogpots in Space, Cowardly Cowardly Cutlass, The Father Christmas Trap, Georgie and the Planet Raider, Harry's Party, Harry with Spots On, Harry the Superhero, Hiccup Harry, Jigger's Day Off, Magic Mash, Monty, the Dog Who Wears Glasses, Mossop's Last Chance, Nora Bone, Private Eye of New York, Our Toilet's Haunted, The Thing-in-a-Box, Two Hoots, Weedy Me, Nina's Machines, →		And Pigs Might Fly, Almost Goodbye, Guzzler, Best Friends, Clever Trevor, Cutlass Rules the Waves, Desparate for a Dog, Ernest the Heroic Lion-Tamer, The Fizziness Business, Free with Every Pack, Ging, Gang, Goolie…, Grandad's Concrete Garden, Grubble Trouble, Harry Moves House, Jacko, Jessy Runs Away, Messages, Monty Bites Back, Monty Must Be Magic, Pesters of the West, Rhyming Russell, Stone the Crows…,		
	Jim and the Sun Goddess, Jim and the Dolphin, ← The Missing Aircraft, Jim in Training, Race for Gold, Rescue Mission, →	The Island of Helos, The Desert Chase, The Sniper of Zimba, Prisoner of Pedro Cay, Danger in the Mountains, The Diamond Smugglers,	The Temple of Mantos, The Shipwreckers, The Killer Rocket, Sabotage in the Arctic,			
			← Johnny Black, Footballer, … Special Agent, … Show-Jumper, … Pilot, … Racing Driver, Johnny Black Stops Dreaming, →			

Title and Publisher	PHASE*	INTEREST AGE	Reading Level A 5^0-5^5	B 5^6-5^{11}	C 6^0-6^5	D 6^6-6^{11}
J						
Journeys into Reading Schofield & Sims	P	5 - 9	← **Level 1:** Two by Two, Fishing, Fingers, Look at Me, So Do I, A House for a Mouse, Supper for a Troll, Signs, → ← **Level 2:** Come On, Find a Pet, Here Comes a Pig …, →		**Level 3:** See a Show, Pick a House, Watch Out …!	**Level 4:** Head In Head Out, Frogs Can't Fly, ← That's Good Joey and the
Jumbo Jets A and C Black	P	7 - 11				
K						
Kathy and Mark Nisbet	P	5 - 9	1. Kathy and Mark,	2. Indoors and Out, 3. Rides and Slides, 4. Something to See, Red Books (4 titles) Blue Books (4 titles)	5. Just Like You, Green Books (4 titles) Orange Books (4 titles)	6. Real and Make Believe, Turquoise Books (4 titles) Plum Books (10 titles)
Kennett Library, The (O/P) Nelson	P/S	10 - 16				
Key Words Mini Hardbacks (Series 641) Ladybird *[formerly Key Words Reading Scheme]*	P	5 - 10	1a Play with Us, 1b Look at This, 1c Read and Write, 2a We Have Fun, 2b Have a Go, 2c I Like to Write,	3a Things We Like, 3b Boys and Girls, 3c Let Me Write, 4a Things We Do, 4b Fun at the Farm, 4c Say the Sound,	5a Where We Go, 5b Out in the Sun, 5c More Sounds to Say, 6a Our Friends, 6b We Like to Help, 6c Reading with Sounds,	7a Happy Holiday, 7b Fun and Games, 7c Easy to Sound,
Key Words Read it Yourself (Series 777) Ladybird	P	5 - 10	Goldilocks, Billy Goats Gruff, Sly Fox …, The Elves …, Hansel and Gretel, Enormous Turnip, Town Mouse, Sleeping Beauty,	Three Little Pigs, Red Riding Hood, Puss in Boots, Dick Whittington, Peter and the Wolf, Rapunzel, The Ugly Duckling, Thumbelina, ← Gingerbread Man, Jack and the Beanstalk, Cinderella, Snow White, The Pied Piper, Wizard of Oz, →	Robinson Crusoe, The Magic Stone, William Tell, Heidi, Magic Paintbrush, Anansea,	
Knight Riders (O/P) Hodder and Stoughton	S	12 - 14+				
Knocklands (Some titles now O/P) Longman	S	11 - 16+				

E 7^0-7^5	F 7^6-7^{11}	G 8^0-8^5	H 8^6-8^{11}	I 9^0-9^5	J 9^6-9^{11}	K 10^0-10^5+
Level 5: See You Later Alligator, Far Away and Long Ago, The Green Street Three, The Moose, ←	→	**Level 6:** Knock at My Door, See for Myself, The Green Street Three Are Back, Simon and His Knockout Yawns, ←	→			
That's Bad, Detectives, ←	→	**Level 7:** Serendipity, The Very Last First, Listen to the Silence, The Something in Thuro Darlay's House, ←	→	→		
			Level 8: Touch the Sky, Journeys Far and Near, Early Morning Water, Bokelia, ←	→		
					The Baked Bean Cure, Charlie and Biff, Sir Quentin Quest Hunts the Jewel, Sir Quentin Quest Hunts the Yeti, Trouble on the Day, Pickles Sniffs it Out, Forecast of Fear, Fergus the Forgetful, Bernie Works a Miracle, ←	→
7. Around the Corner, 8. All Through the Year, Lime Books (10 titles) Cherry Books (10 titles)	**New Extension Readers/Kathy and Mark Extension Readers** From Faraway Places,	← Horizons	Trade Winds, Treasures, Life Lines, → ← Links,	Landscapes, → ← Crossroads,	→ ← Changes,	Seven Seas, Currents, →
				Short Series Grade 1: 5 titles The Coral Island, Treasure Island, etc. Grade 2: 4 titles A Christmas Carol, David Copperfield, etc. ←	→	Grades 3 and 4: 4 titles The Count of Monte Christo, Jane Eyre, etc. Grades 3 and 4: 7 titles The Last of the Mohicans, Ben Hur, etc.
					Long Series Grades 1 and 2: 5 titles Children of the New Forest, White Fang, etc. ← **Modern Series** 9 titles The Red Beret, Cockleshell Heroes, Exploration Fawcett, etc. ←	→
8a Sunny Days, 8b The Big House, 8c Fun with Sounds,	9a Games We Like, 9b Jump from the Sky, 9c Enjoying Reading,	10a Adventure on the Island, 10b Adventure at the Castle, 10c Learning is Fun,	11a Mystery on the Island, 11b The Carnival, 11c Books Are Exciting,	12a The Holiday Camp Mystery, 12b Mountain Adventure, 12c Open Door to Reading,		
			Level 1: 4 titles A Night to Forget, Hostage, etc. ←	→	**Level 2:** 4 titles The Room Upstairs, Blue Valley High, etc. ←	→ **Level 3:** 4 titles Escape to Danger, etc.
		Level 2: Red Save the Last Dance for Me, etc. **Level 1:** Blue Cave Rescue, Dead Man's Creek, House of Fear,		**Level 4:** Green Backs Lesley's Life, Will of Iron, The Six Getting By, Silvertown Disaster, etc. ←	→	
			Level 3: Pink Backs Love Stories, Hooked!, The Balaclava Story, Pickled Onions, etc. ←	→	**Level 5:** Black Backs Time Rope (4 books), Long Journey Home, Waves, Home Truths, Walking Shadows, etc. ←	→

L

Title and Publisher	PHASE*	INTEREST AGE	Reading Level A 5^0-5^5	B 5^6-5^{11}	C 6^0-6^5	D 6^6-6^{11}
Ladybird Graded Readers (Series 873) Ladybird	P	6 - 10			← **Grade 1:** The Enormous Turnip, Billy Goats Gruff, Goldilocks, Hansel and Gretel, The Sly Fox and the Red Hen, The Elves and the Shoemaker, → (spans C–D)	
Language Patterns (O/P) Harcourt Brace	P/S	5 - 12	**Readiness Stage:** 10 titles Kate and Fluffy Books, Fluffy's Aeroplane, etc.	**Stage 1:** 4 titles Animal Friends, ← It's Fun, → (spans B–C)	It's Magic,	Happy Ever After, **Stage 2:** 4 titles Tiny Toils,
Laura Brewster Books (O/P) Murray	S	13 - 18				
Leaders (Series 737) (O/P) Ladybird	P/S	6 - 14				
Legends (Series 741) Ladybird	P	6 - 10				
Let's Celebrate (O/P) Ginn	P	6 - 10				
Let's Find Out About ... (O/P) Watts	P	5 - 9				
Let's Go (O/P) Watts	P	6 - 9				
Letterland Collins (T, S, AU, V, IT, RR)	P	6 - 9			Eddy Elephant, Flat Hats, Impy Ink, Oscar Orange, Uppy Umbrella, Oscar's Brother, Annie Apple, I Am, Help Get the Hat, Where Are You? Ducklings, Who Has? Peter's Pictures, The Picnic,	Five Vowel Man, Rebecca and Heidi's Story, Firefly's Light, What Do You Like to Eat? Twins at the Zoo, Bits of Fur, Granny's Shawl, Eager Seal, Twins, Be Good, Ridiculous,
Library Bookshelves Collins	P	5 - 11		← **Bookshelf A:** 40 titles from Picture Lions series → (spans B–D)		

<table>
<tr><th>E
7^{0}-7^{5}</th><th>F
7^{6}-7^{11}</th><th>G
8^{0}-8^{5}</th><th>H
8^{6}-8^{11}</th><th>I
9^{0}-9^{5}</th><th>J
9^{6}-9^{11}</th><th>K
10^{0}-10^{5}+</th></tr>
<tr><td colspan="2">Grade 2:
Town Mouse and Country Mouse,
The Ugly Duckling, Three Little Pigs,
Red Riding Hood, Peter and the Wolf,
Rapunzel,</td><td></td><td colspan="2">Grade 4:
Cinderella, Pinocchio, The Sorcerer's Apprentice,
The Jungle Book, The Secret Garden, Tom Sawyer,
Heidi,
Wizard of Oz,</td><td></td><td></td></tr>
<tr><td></td><td colspan="2">Grade 3:
The Pied Piper …, The Magic Stone,
Jack and the Beanstalk, Gingerbread Man,</td><td></td><td></td><td></td><td></td></tr>
<tr><td colspan="2">Animals from Everywhere,</td><td colspan="2">Stories Old and New,</td><td colspan="2">Here and There,</td><td>Fact Fable and Fantasy</td></tr>
<tr><td></td><td colspan="2">Step by Step,</td><td colspan="2">Stage 3: 2 titles
Believe It or Not,</td><td colspan="2">Stage 4:
To and Fro,</td></tr>
<tr><td></td><td></td><td></td><td></td><td>L
10^{6}-10^{11}</td><td>M
11^{0}-11^{5}</td><td>N
11^{6}-11^{11}</td></tr>
<tr><td></td><td></td><td></td><td></td><td colspan="2">Stage 5 Along the Way</td><td>Stage 6 All Sorts,</td></tr>
<tr><td></td><td></td><td></td><td></td><td>(Language and Patterns, continued)</td><td>Moving On,</td><td>Further Afield,</td></tr>
<tr><td></td><td></td><td colspan="2">1. House of Laughs, 2. Killer Music,
3. Tiger Rose, 4. Fast-Food King, 5. Falling Star,
6. Golden Idol,</td><td></td><td></td><td></td></tr>
<tr><td colspan="2">39 titles including:
Water Ducks and Swans,
Man in the Air,
Man and his Car, etc.</td><td></td><td></td><td></td><td></td><td></td></tr>
<tr><td></td><td></td><td>Robin Hood,</td><td>Aladdin,
Ali Baba,
King Arthur,</td><td>Famous Legends,
(Books 1 and 2)</td><td></td><td></td></tr>
<tr><td></td><td></td><td>Harvest,
Weddings,
Birthdays,
Storybook,</td><td>Spring,
Friends,</td><td></td><td></td><td></td></tr>
<tr><td colspan="2">16 titles:
Animals of Africa, Babies, Bees, Butterflies,
Christmas, Clothes, etc.</td><td></td><td></td><td></td><td></td><td></td></tr>
<tr><td></td><td></td><td colspan="2">Let's Go: 23 titles including:
The Airport,
The Bank,
The Garage,
The Doctor,
The Dentist,
etc.
Let's Go Countries
America,
Antarctica,
Belgium, etc.
36 titles so far</td><td></td><td></td><td></td></tr>
<tr><td>Fred's Flippers,
Noisy Nick,
Harry's Hats,
Lucy's List,
Really Ruined,
Bija's Story,
Surprise for Mrs. I,
Letterland Race Day,
Bouncy Ben and the Black Thing,
Do You Wonder?
Lost Yo-Yo's,
King's Breakfast,
Munching Mike's Meal,</td><td>Buzzing and Oozing,
Grandad's Garden,
Long Song,</td><td></td><td></td><td></td><td></td><td></td></tr>
<tr><td colspan="3">Bookshelf B:
40 titles from Lion and Amanda series</td><td colspan="4">Bookshelf C:
40 titles from Lion and Amanda series</td></tr>
</table>

L

Title and Publisher	PHASE*	INTEREST AGE	Reading Level A 5^{0}-5^{5}	B 5^{6}-5^{11}	C 6^{0}-6^{5}	D 6^{6}-6^{11}
Library Corner Ginn	P	8 - 11				
Link Up Collins (T, S)	P	5 - 9	**Starter Books** 1-12 Things at Home, Things We Eat, Things in School, Pets, Wild Animals, Playing, People at Work, etc. **Main Readers** 1. Look Around, **Build-Up Books** Sa. Hill Street, Sb. Drivers, Sc. The Police Car, 1a. Park Street, 1b. Going to School, 1c. My Day,	2. Just Like Me, ← 3. Friends, (B–C) → 2a. Shopping, 2b. Along the Street, 2c. Karen at the Zoo,	← 4. Naughty Nicky's Book, (C–D) → 3a. Gran's Birthday, 3b. The Runaway Van, 3c. Silly Children,	5. Robert and Linda, 4a. Naughty Nicky Runs Away, 4b. Naughty Nicky and the Yellow Car, 4c. Aunt Lee in Hospital, 5a. The Story of Goldie, 5b. Three Little Rabbits, 5c. Robert Finds Danny,
Listen and Look Ginn (RR)	P	5 - 7	Follow the Leader, How Many Legs?. Who Wears this Hat?, Kitten Chased a Fly,	What's the Time Mr. Wolf? Where Are the Car Keys? Here's a House, Houses,	Where Can Pussy Sleep? I'm Not I'm Not, Where is Bear? Let's Go,	
Listening and Reading Penguin (AU)	P/S	7 - 12				**Stage 1:** 7 titles Adventures of the Little Wooden Horse, The Iron Man, Lion at School, Mr. Miacca,
Literacy Links Kingscourt Publishing *[Traditional Tales, Poems and Rhymes, Contemporary Stages.]* (T, S, RR)	P	5 - 11	← **Stage 1** (64 titles) (A–B) →	← **Stage 2** (64 titles) (B–D) →		**Stage 3** (64 titles) **Set A** **Set A**

E 7^0-7^5	F 7^6-7^{11}	G 8^0-8^5	H 8^6-8^{11}	I 9^0-9^5	J 9^6-9^{11}	K 10^0-10^5+
	Set 1: The Lucky Feather, The Duck in the Gun, The Spider in the Show, Captain Felonius, Giant on the Bus, Miss Mouse Gets Married, Tug of War,	The Dragon's Birthday, Brith the Terrible, The Fierce Little Woman …, **Set 2:** Magic Mill, Who Will Be the Sun? Tortoise's Dream, What Made Tiddalik Laugh, **Set 3:** The Baby Sitter, Donkey, **Set 4:** Crafty Jackal,	How Night Came, Mouse Deers Market, Yellow Overalls, What a Way, Big Fish, Little Fish,			
Story Club Twig's House, The Two Snowmen, The Witch of the Forest, Mouse Medicine, 6. Away from Home, ← 7. Far and Wide, → 6a. The King Who Wanted …, 6b. The Lonely Scarecrow, 6c. The Lion and the Mouse,	The Seagull's Picnic, The Little Submarine, Durga's Secret, The Missing Nuts, 8. Round the World, 7a. The Magic Stone, 7b. The Tortoise and the Baboon, 7c. The Midnight Dancer, 8a. A Kitten to Keep, 8b. Flip in School, 8c. Mr. Clementine's Cats,	Mr. Tweedle's New Hat, The Wishing Apple, Naughty Mini Bear, Emma's Hamster, 9. Surprises, 9a. The Island, 9b. The Rocking Horse, 9c. The Baby Seal,	Mr. Tweedle's Old Coat, The Magic Cat, Lazy Tim, Abu and Lulu, 10. Magic Mixture,			
(+ cassettes) The Thingummijig, Shadrach, The Wolf and the Seven Little Kids,	**Stage 2:** 7 titles (+ cassettes) The Poltergoose, Return to Air, Robinson Crusoe, Stig of the Dump, James and the Giant Peach, The Cave of the Cyclops, The Balaclava Story,					
Set B **Set C** **Set D** **Set E** **Stage 4** (64 titles) **Set B** **Set C** ← **Set D** → **Stage 5** (32 titles) ← **Sets A, B, C and D** →	**Set E** **Stage 6** (32 titles) ← **Sets A, B, C and D** →		**Sets A and B**	**Stage 7** (24 titles) ← **Sets C and D** → **Stage 8** (24 titles) ← **Sets A, B, C and D** →		

L

Title and Publisher	PHASE*	INTEREST AGE	Reading Level A 5^{0}-5^{5}	B 5^{6}-5^{11}	C 6^{0}-6^{5}	D 6^{6}-6^{11}
Little Readers (O/P) Collins	P	4 - 6	Little Readers (10 books) Little Steps to Reading (10 books)			
Livelihoods Nelson	S	11 - 16				
Lively Readers (O/P) Nelson	P/S	8 - 14				
Livewire Chillers (formerly Chillers) Hodder and Stoughton/ Basic Skills Agency (AU)	S	13 - 16				
Living in the Past (O/P) (Blackwell) Simon and Schuster	P/S	9 - 13				
Longman Book Project Longman (T, S, AU)	P/S	7 - 12				
Longman Classics Longman	P/S	10 - 16				
Longman Movieworld Longman	S	12 - 16				
Longman Reading World Longman	P/S	4 - 12+	**Level 1:** 1. The Sandwich, 2. The Picnic, 3. Goodnight, 4. The Trumpet, 5. Fred's Mess, 6. Tea Time, 7. Fred's Shelf, 8. Pancakes!, 9. Over and Under…, 10. Sadie, Spider, 11. The Joggers, 12. Ghost, Ghost…, 13. Have You Seen Stanley?, 14. Sadie, Spider, Strikes Again, 15. Go Away Stanley, 16. The Jumper, **Levels 1-3** At Home Books, **Level 2** More Books (10 titles)		**Level 2:** 1. Nobody, 2. The Grumble, 3. What if a Bear Comes? 4. Christmas, 5. The Cat and The Witch, 6. Fred's Birthday, 7. The Chimney, 8. Clean up Your Room, 9. Stanley Goes to School, 10. The Secret, 11. Get Some Bread Fred, 12. Garden Rain,	13. Lonely Stanley 14. Who's Asked 15. Fred's 16. April 17. Ghost, Ghost, 18. The Grumble 19. The Grumble 20. Cat Tricks, 21. Fishing, 22. Milk Oh!, 23. Squirrel 24. Litterbug, 25. A Sunflower 26. Fred's Photo **Level 3:** 1. Lily and the Vacuum Cleaner, 2. The Dinosaur Race, 3. Poor Rabbit, 4. Witch Tricks, 5. Oh Stanley!

E 7^0-7^5	F 7^6-7^{11}	G 8^0-8^5	H 8^6-8^{11}	I 9^0-9^5	J 9^6-9^{11}	K 10^0-10^5+
				← Apprentice Jockey, High Speed Train Driver, Red Devil, Cordon Blue Cook, →		
1. Treasure, 2. Car Racing, 3. Migration, 4. Man on the Moon, 5. Dolphins, 6. Test Pilot,	7. Telling the Time, 8. Across the Ocean, 10. The Weather,	9. Skin Diving, 11. Getting the Message, 12. Canals, ← 14. Looking at the Sky, 16. On the Air, →	13. Earthquakes and Volcanoes, 15. Game Warden,			
			← Chillers 1, Chillers 2, Chillers 3, Chillers 4, Chillers 5, →			
				Britons and Romans, The Dark Ages, The Middle Ages, Tudor Times, Stuarts and Georgians, Domesday, The Victorians,		
	Fiction 2 **Band 1** (8 titles) **Band 2** (8 titles)	← **Band 3** (7 titles) →			← **Band 4** (7 titles) →	**Fiction 3 - Band 1** (7 titles) **Band 2** (8 titles), **Band 3** (8 titles), **Band 4** (7 titles), **Fiction 4 - Band 1** (5 titles), **Band 2** (5 titles), **Band 3** (5 titles), **Band 4** (5 titles)
	Stage 1: Alice in Wonderland, Black Beauty, King Arthur, etc.	**Stage 2:** Round the World in Eighty Days, A Christmas Carol, Kidnapped, etc.	**Stage 3:** Dr. Jekyll and Mr. Hyde, Dracula, Return of Sherlock Holmes, etc.	**Stage 4:** Lorna Doone, Oliver Twist, Jane Eyre, etc.		
	The Poseidon Adventure, Star Wars, The Silver Streak,	Jaws 2, Rollercoaster, The 39 Steps,				
Level 4: 1. Bony-Legs, 2. School Days…, 3. Surprise Parties, 4. Meet M & M, 5. Quack! Quack!…, the Ants? Snowman, Fool, Are You Ever Lonely? Goes Jogging, Goes For a Walk, → is Lonely, Named Bert, Album, 6. The Bracelet, 7. Toad Road, 8. Don't Be Silly…, → 9. Jimmy James, 10. Rosie's New Pet,	6. Sneezy Snatcher, 7. Elephants, 8. Vardiello…, 9. Goodies and Baddies, 10. That's Strange!,	**Level 5:** 1. Animal Pie, 2. Interesting Things, 3. Fun and Games, 4. Villains All!, 5. A Marvellous Mix,	6. Mostly Magic, 7. Brave as a Lion, 8. Crooks Galore!, 9. Animal Antics, 10. It Was a Nightmare!, **Level 6:** 1. Secrets to Share, 2. A Python for a Pet, 3. The TV War,	← 4. Going…Going…Gone! 5. Running Away, 6. Outlawed!, → **Level 7:** ← 1. Sense of Mystery 2. Tales out of School, 3. Some You Win, **Level 8:** ← 1. Trapped, 2. Work it Out!, 3. Test of Courage,	4. Fearful Journeys, → 5. Stange Worlds, 4. Away from Home, 5. In Times of War, →	

Title and Publisher	PHASE*	INTEREST AGE	Reading Level A 5^{0}-5^{5}	B 5^{6}-5^{11}	C 6^{0}-6^{5}	D 6^{6}-6^{11}
L						
Look at … Books Ginn	P	6 - 10				
Look Book Nature Activity Readers Philip and Tacey	P	5 - 9				
Looking at Geography (O/P) A and C Black	P/S	8 - 14				
Looking at History (O/P) A and C Black	P/S	9 - 14				
Look Out Gang, The Gibson	P/S	10 - 14				1. The Gang Meets,
M						
Macdonald Young Books Wayland Publishers (RR)	P	4 - 8				
Macmillan Beginners (O/P) Macmillan	P	5 - 7+			← The Farm, The Show, The Circus, The Zoo, Sports, Hobbies, Shopping, My Teeth, Toys and Games, Firefighters, →	
Macmillan Junior Geography (O/P) Nelson	P	7 - 10				
Magic Bean Heinemann (RR)	P	4 - 11			Sand, Angus Thought He Was Big,	**Strand A -** Mr. Taddle's Hat, Stuck in the Mud, **Strand B -** Andrea's Cubby, Two Feet, Never Snap at a Bubble, Eeny Meeny, Miney Mouse, **Strand C -** Claude Money, Sleepy on Sunday, Which Way Now?

	E 7^0-7^5	F 7^6-7^{11}	G 8^0-8^5	H 8^6-8^{11}	I 9^0-9^5	J 9^6-9^{11}	K 10^0-10^5+
L	**First Series:** Look at ... ... An Apple, ... A Bean, ... An Egg,	... A Spider, ... A Ball of Wool, ... An Ice Lolly,	**Second Series:** ... A Pen; ... A Coin; ... A Watch; ... A Lamp; ... A Telephone; ... Frozen Peas,				
	← 12 titles: The Harvest Mouse, The Swan, The Hedgehog, The Red Squirrel, The Rabbit, The Robin Redbreast, The Honey Bees, etc. → (spans E–G)						
					← Looking at Other Children, (O/P) Looking at Everyday Things, (O/P) Looking at Britain, Looking at the World Today, (O/P) Looking at Scotland, The Hiroshima Story, West Indies, Follow the Map, → (spans I–J)		
				← 1. From Cavemen to Vikings, 2. The Middle Ages, 3. Tudors and Stuarts, (O/P) 4. Queen Anne to Queen Victoria, 5. The Twentieth Century, **Looking at Ancient History** Egypt and Mesopotamia, → (spans H–I)			
	2. The Gang and the Pay Grab, 3. The Gang and the Mail Train Robbers, 4. The Gang and the Stolen Bicycles,	5. The Gang and the Smuggler, 6. The Gang and the Airport Car Thieves,					
M	**Picture Books** Chloe's Eggs, Mole in a Hole, The Owl and the Pussycat, That New Dress,	Animal Stories, Haddock, The Jolly Witch, The Little Apple Tree, Mrs Smith's Crocodile, Six Dinner Sid,			**Yellow Storybooks** I Want That Pony, Baby Bug, Khumalo's Blanket, Wishing Bird and Co., Gilly the Kid, Beach Baby, Hurray for Monty Ray, Tall Tale Tom, Polly Thumb, **Red Storybooks** Birdy and the Ghosties, Dreamy Daniel, Brainy Bert, The Four-legged Sheriff, The Ghost of Joseph Grey, Hopping Mad, Judy and the Martian, Nigel the Pirate, Lizzy's War, The Midnight Moropus, Princess by Mistake, The Queen Cat, T.V. Genie, Tanya, Hoofed Crusader, Wonderwitch, Wonderwitch and the Rooftop Cats, (spans I–J)		Fair's Fair, The Firetail Cat, The King in the Forest, Matthew and the Sea Singer, Mog and Bumble, Mr Dunfilling and the Toothy Monster, Rent-a-Friend, Thomas and the Tinners, The Twitches on Horriday, The Thing in the Sink,
						1. How We Live, 2. At Home and Abroad, ← 3. About the World, → (spans J–K)	4. In Britain Now,
	Choices and Decisions (Infant Fiction) Help! Wild Rose, Huggly, Snuggly Pets, No Lion At All,		Little Brown Monkey, Timothy Toad,				
	Social Living (Infant Fiction) Fred Told Me, So What,	The Cockatoo,					
	The Language of Maths (Infant Fiction) In the Middle of the Night,	Down They Rolled, The Tiniest Hippo,	One Wobbly Wheelbarrow,	**Stand D - The Environment (Infant Fiction)** Amos Well's Shop, Duck in Danger, The Rowd-etty House, Deep in a Forest, Shut the Door, Changing Shape, The One-Eyed Zoff, Looks Like Lunch,	**Junior Novels** Wild Card, Gelati Supreme, One Week with my Grandmother, Phoebe's Inheritence,	Letters to Leak, The Mystery of the Missing Garden Gnome, Brolga,	The Chums of Thomas Filbett, Skool Suks, Seb and Sasha, Dust in my Eyes, Making Best,

M

Title and Publisher	PHASE*	INTEREST AGE	Reading Level A 5^0-5^5	B 5^6-5^{11}	C 6^0-6^5	D 6^6-6^{11}
M Books (Macmillan) Nelson	S	12 - 18				
Methuen Paperbacks (O/P) Methuen *[This series is entitled Pied Piper Books in the hardback edition.]*	P	8 - 11				
Mister Books, Fabbri	P	4 - 7	← 7 titles →			
Moggy Books (O/P) Ginn	P	6 - 11				**First Series:** Moggy's Seaside Opposites, Moggy Goes on a Picnic, Moggy Bakes Some Bread, Moggy Builds a Beehive, **Second Series:** Moggy Keeps Fit, Moggy Flies a Kite, Moggy Grows Some Vegetables, Moggy Builds a Bridge,
Monster Books Longman	P	6 - 11				
Moonstones Cambridge University Press	P/S	8 - 12				
My Belief Franklin Watts	P/S	9 - 14+				
My Country (O/P) Wayland *[Easier reading edition of Living Here Series]*	P/S	9 - 14				
My World (O/P) Nelson	P	5 - 8		**Red** Set 1: 12 titles My Cat, The Cat Family, My Dog, Working Dogs, My Pony, Working Horses, etc. Set 2: 12 titles Cows on the Farm, Cows and Milk, Chickens on the Farm, Chickens and Eggs, etc.	**Green** Set 1: 12 titles Rabbit's Day, Baby Rabbits, Beaver's Day, Beaver's Home, Red Squirrel, Grey Squirrel, etc. Set 2: 12 titles Different Kinds of Bears, Grizzly Bears, Tortoiseshell Butterflies, Butterflies and Moths, Kangaroo's Home, etc.	**Blue** Set 1: 12 titles My Home in Russia, My Home in Australia, Set 2: 12 titles My Home in Japan, My Home in Italy, etc.

<table>
<tr><th>E
7^0-7^5</th><th>F
7^6-7^{11}</th><th>G
8^0-8^5</th><th>H
8^6-8^{11}</th><th>I
9^0-9^5</th><th>J
9^6-9^{11}</th><th>K
10^0-10^5+</th></tr>
<tr><td></td><td></td><td></td><td></td><td></td><td></td><td>40 titles (10^0-11^5)
Dragon Slayer,
After the Goatman,
The Cats, Fish,
The Eighteenth Emergency,
The Crane,
My Side of the Mountain,
I Am David,
Time Trap,
Horned Helmet,
The Pinballs, etc.</td></tr>
<tr><td></td><td></td><td></td><td></td><td colspan="2">Michael Hardcastle: 4 titles
In the Net, Away from Home, etc.
Brian Earnshaw: 4 titles
Dragonfall 5 and the Royal Beast, etc.
Mabel Allen: 4 titles
The Wood Street Secret,
The Wood Street Group, etc.</td><td></td></tr>
<tr><td></td><td></td><td></td><td></td><td></td><td></td><td></td></tr>
<tr><td></td><td></td><td></td><td></td><td></td><td></td><td></td></tr>
<tr><td>1 - 12
Monster Comes to the City,
etc.</td><td>13 - 24
Monster and the Mural,
etc.</td><td>25 - 30
Lady Monster and the Pet Shop,
etc.</td><td></td><td></td><td></td><td></td></tr>
<tr><td></td><td></td><td></td><td colspan="2">20 titles so far including:
Maggot Pie,
Ranjit and the Mighty Mini-bus,
The Yesterday Girl,
Alvanez and the Golden Treasure,
The Rain Forest Storybook, etc.,</td><td></td><td></td></tr>
<tr><td></td><td></td><td></td><td colspan="3">I Am an Anglican, ... a Jew, ... a Muslim,
... a Buddhist, ... a Greek Orthodox,
... a Sikh, ... a Hindu, ... a Rastafarian,
... a Roman Catholic, ... a Pentecostal,</td><td></td></tr>
<tr><td></td><td></td><td colspan="2">13 titles: Argentina is My Country,
Brazil, Canada, Denmark, France, Greece,
India, Kenya, Pakistan, Spain, etc.</td><td></td><td></td><td></td></tr>
<tr><td>A Day Out in Russia,
The Australian Outback,

New Year in Japan,
The Regatta in Venice,</td><td></td><td></td><td></td><td></td><td></td><td></td></tr>
</table>

Title and Publisher	PHASE*	INTEREST AGE	Reading Level A 5^{0}-5^{5}	B 5^{6}-5^{11}	C 6^{0}-6^{5}	D 6^{6}-6^{11}
N **Newsmakers** Hodder and Stoughton	S	12 - 16				
New Story Books Nisbet	P	5 - 8				**Plum Group** 1. How the Bear Lost His Tail, 2. The Pigeon and the Nut, 3. The Beetle and the Mouse, 4. The Cat Who Went to London, 5. The Great Race, 6. The King and the Moon, 7. The Strong Little Bird, 8. The Three Wishes, 9. Ivan and the Golden Goose, 10. The Elves and the Shoemaker,
New Wave Readers Heinemann (AU)	S	12 - 16				
New Way (Macmillan) Nelson *[A new series of Gay Way Readers.]*	P	5 - 8	**White Level** Big Book, Six Little Books Without Words, Six Little Books With Words, Easy Start - Set A, Easy Start - Set B, Parallel Books - Six Little Books With Words, ← **Red Level**: Counters → (A–B) ← **Red Level**: Peppers → (A–B)	**Pink Level** Easy Start - Set A, Easy Start - Set B, Core Book - Meet the Friends, Platform Books - 8 titles, Parallel Books - 8 titles, ← **Red Level:** My Poetry Book - A Coloured Bridge, → (B–C)	**Red Level** ← Easy Start - Set A, → (C–D) ← Easy Start - Set B, → (C–D) Core Book - Fat Pig's Birthday, ← Platform Books - 8 titles → (C–D) ← Parallel Books - 8 titles → (C–D) **Green Level** ← Easy Start - Set A, → (C–D) ← Easy Start - Set B, → (C–D) ← **Blue Level:** My Poetry Book - This Morning My Dad Shouted, → (C–D) ← **Green Level:** Counters → (C–D) ← **Green Level:** Peppers → (C–D)	
New Windmill Series Heinemann *[Now included in New Windmill Book Boxes.]*	P	9 - 14				
O **Olga da Polga** (O/P) Longman	P	6 - 9				
Once Upon a Time (O/P) Ginn	P	5 - 9				

E 7^{0}-7^{5}	F 7^{6}-7^{11}	G 8^{0}-8^{5}	H 8^{6}-8^{11}	I 9^{0}-9^{5}	J 9^{6}-9^{11}	K 10^{0}-10^{5}+
				← Newsmakers 1, 2 and 3 →		
Lime Group 1. The Tiger and the Farmer, 2. Peter and the Troll, 3. The Jewel Tears, 4. Tim and the Leprechaun, 5. The Wonderful Garden, 6. Abu and Amina, 7. The Little Golden Fish, 8. The Bronze Giant, 9. Rapunzel, 10. The Siamese Cats,	**Cherry Group** 1. The Cap o'Rushes, 2. The Dancing Princesses, 3. The Pekinese Dog, 4. Kate Crackernuts, 5. Little Freddy and His Fiddle, 6. Conrad and His Brothers, 7. Bob and the Knockers, 8. The Flying Horse, 9. East of the Sun…, 10. Eric and the Sea Snake,					
	Sheela and the Robbers, Dancing Shoes,	The Singer Not the Song, Born to Run,	Murder at Mortlock Hall, The Last Recording, Clara, Countdown to Midnight,	One Pair of Eyes, ← Poor Little Rich Girl, The Colombian Connection, Star Picture, Zargon Zoo, →		Brilliant!, Fire, Bookshop Trick, Kate's Revenge, Double Danger, Karateka,
Green Level Core Book - Bad Cow, Platform Books - 8 titles Parallel Books - 8 titles **Violet Level:** My Poetry Book, Where Wild Things Grow,	**Blue Level** Core Book - Dressing Up, Platform Books - 8 titles Parallel Books - 8 titles **Yellow Level** Core Book - Terrible Tiger,	**Violet Level** Core Book - The Kind Prince, Platform Books - 4 titles Parallel Books - 4 titles **Yellow Level** Platform Books - 4 titles, Parallel Books - 4 titles, **Orange Level** Core Book - The Bank Robbery,	**Orange Level** Platform Books - 4 titles, Parallel Books - 4 titles,			
					Many titles: Examples: The Latchkey Children, The Witch's Daughter, The Saturdays, The Railway Children, A Handful of Thieves, Conrad's War, The BFG, The Overland Launch, The Finding, Run for Your Life, The Silver Sword, The Eighteenth Emergency, The Cartoonist, Matilda, The Pinballs, Charlie and the Chocolate Factory, 100 and 1 Dalmations, The Enchanted Island, The Haunting, The Daydreamer, No More School, Chicken,	
Set A: 4 titles Olga Makes a Wish, etc. **Set B:** 4 titles Olga Takes a Bite, etc.						
	Goldilocks …, Cinderella,	Beauty and the Beast, The Three Little Pigs, Rumpelstiltskin, Hansel and Gretel, Princess and the Pea,	Snow White …, The Tinder Box, Sleeping Beauty, The Frog Prince,	The Twelve Dancing Princesses,		

Title and Publisher	PHASE*	INTEREST AGE	Reading Level A 5^0-5^5	B 5^6-5^{11}	C 6^0-6^5	D 6^6-6^{11}
O **One, Two, Three and Away!** Collins	P	5 - 10	**Grandmother Yellow - hat's Picture Books** Set 1: Poor Mr. Blue Hat, When the Moon ..., The Man and the Tiger, The Flowers in the River, Set 2: Splash in the River, Sarah Ann ..., The Monster in the Lake, The King Tree ..., **Pre-Readers** 1-4 1A-4A 5-8 5A-8A 9-12 **Introductory Books** Set A-D Set E-H ← Set I-L Set M-P →	**Main Books: Green** 1. The Village with Three Corners, 1A. The Old Man and the Wind, 1B. Gopal and the Little White Cat, ← 2. Billy Blue-hat and the Duck Pond, 2A. The Cat and the Feather, 2B. Roger and the Ghost, → **Platform Readers** Blue Set 1-6 Set 7-10 ← Blue Set 11-16 Green Set 1-6 Set 7-10 →	**Red** 3. The Haystack 3A. The Donkey, 3B. The Empty House, ← 4. The Island in Deep River, 4A. The Two Giants, 4B. The House in the Corner of the Wood, → Red Set 1-10	**Yellow** 5. The Cat's Dance, 6. The Stepping Stones, Yellow Set 1-6 Set 7-10
One World (O/P) Watts	P/S	8 - 12				
Open Door Nelson	P	5 - 9+	Fun Books (16 titles) Stage 1 Red 1 - 6	Stage 1 Red 7 - 12 Stage 2 Blue 1 - 9	Stage 3 Yellow 1 - 7 Stage 2 Blue 10 - 16	Stage 3 Yellow 8 - 10
Oranges and Lemons Simon and Schuster	P	6 - 9+				
Our Culture Franklin Watts	P	6 - 10				

E 7^{0}-7^{5}	F 7^{6}-7^{11}	G 8^{0}-8^{5}	H 8^{6}-8^{11}	I 9^{0}-9^{5}	J 9^{6}-9^{11}	K 10^{0}-10^{5}+
Yellow 7. Billy Blue-hat's Day, ← 8. The White Owls, →	9. The Lost Dog, ← 10. The Three Robbers, →	11. A Boat on Deep River, 12. The House in Dark Woods,				
			← I Am Blind, I Have Asthma, I Am Deaf, I Have Diabetes, I Have Down's Syndrome, I Have Spina Bifida, I Have Cerebral Palsy, I Have Cystic Fibrosis, →			
Stage 4 Green 1 - 6	Stage 4 Green 7 - 10	Stage 5 Grey Miss Monk's Class, A Cat called Rover, What I'd Really Like, Spacemen and Spooks, ← Stage 5 Grey The Lost Puppy, Stuck!, Into the Ark, The Vampire's Breakfast, etc., →	Stage 5 Grey The Greedy Green Grunter, The Golden Phoenix,			
Level O **Oranges** (6 titles) A Pigeon Called Zonk, Flash's Adventures, etc.	**Level O** **Lemons** (6 titles) Nazeem's Cat, Kirsty's Budgie, etc. **Level 1** **Oranges** The Bear and the Boaster, The Bear and the Hare, Milly-Jilly and the Bear, **Lemons** Black and White Skin, Thick Skins,	Bear Squash-you-all-flat, The Bear and the Mushrooms, Australian Animals, Shells and Pickles, Pretty Tough, Where Did Our Legs Go? **Level 2** **Oranges** Frizzel's Birthday Surprise, Frizzel's Ballet Dancer, Frizzel Learns to Swim, **Lemons** The Beginnings of the Earth, Age of the Mammals, The First People, **Level 3** **Lemons** (6 titles) Unsinkable Ship, Buried Alive, etc. **Level 4** **Oranges** (6 titles) Destroy, Grey Oaks, etc.	Frizzel the Ambulance Driver, Frizzel the Supercook, Frizzel's Sports Day, Life Begins on Earth, Lizards and Things, Age of the Dinosaurs, **Oranges** (6 titles) A Home for Little Moonbear, How Light Came to Earth, etc. **Lemons** (6 titles) Actress, Archaeologist, etc.			
← Buddhist, Hindu, Jew, Muslim, Rastafarian, Sikh, →						

O

Title and Publisher	PHASE*	INTEREST AGE	Reading Level A 5^0-5^5	B 5^6-5^{11}	C 6^0-6^5	D 6^6-6^{11}
Oxford Graded Readers Oxford University Press	P/S	9 - 14				
Oxford Junior English Oxford University Press	P/S	9 - 13				
Oxford Junior History Oxford University Press	P/S	9 - 13				
Oxford Reading Tree Oxford University Press (T, S, AU, V, IT, RR)	P	5 - 7+	**Stage 1** Flop over Book, **Picture Storybooks** Kipper Storybooks (6 titles), Biff and Chip Storybooks (6 titles), **Extended Stories** Kipper, Biff and Chip,	**Stage 2** **Storybooks** (6 titles), The Toy's Party, A New Dog, etc.,	**Stage 2** **More Stories** Pack A - (6 titles), Pack B - (6 titles), **Extended Stories** Pack A, Pack B,	
			Wrens (Stage 2 and 3) **Wrens Stage 2** Storybooks (6 titles), **More Wrens** Stage 2 **Wrens Stage 3** Storybooks (6 titles), Extended Stories (6 titles),			
				Stage 3 **Storybooks** (6 titles), On the Sand, The Rope Swing, etc.,	**Stage 3** **More Stories** Pack A (6 titles), Pack B (6 titles),	
			Branch Library **Wildsmith Books** Pack A (6 titles),		**Stage 4** **Storybooks** (6 titles), House for Sale, The New House, etc.,	**Stage** **More** Pack A Pack B **Extended** Pack A, Pack B,
					Sparrows (Stages 3 and 4 supplementaries) **Stage 3** Storybooks (6 titles),	**Stage 4** Storybooks (6 titles), **More Sparrows** Storybooks (6 titles),
					Branch Library **Lydia Books** Pack A (6 titles),	**Stage 5** **Storybooks** (6 titles) The Magic Key, Pirate Adventure, etc., **Woodpeckers Anthology** The Sun Ship, **Branch Library** **Victor Books** Pack A (6 titles)

E 7^0-7^5	F 7^6-7^{11}	G 8^0-8^5	H 8^6-8^{11}	I 9^0-9^5	J 9^6-9^{11}	K 10^0-10^5+
"Junior" Level [examples from 30 titles] →	He Cannot Really Read, The Muster,	Dick Turpin, The Ruined House, The Dragon's Head, Moses,	Missing, Another Adventure in London,			
"Senior" Level [examples from 24 titles] →	The Good Man, Fire in the Bush, Smuggler's Island, Kit Carson,	The Black Case, Adventure in London, Black Beauty,	Little Women, A Life of Her Own,			
			← Joan of Arc, The Story of Trains, →			
		← To Catch a Thief, →				
	← Book 2 Food and Farms →		← 3. The Coastline, →			
← Book 1 Introduction →				← 4. Homes and Shelters, 5. Our Language, →		
					← 1. The Invaders, 2. The Middle Ages, 3. The Tudors and Stuarts, 4. Britain Becomes a Great Power, 5. The Modern Age, 6. The Twentieth Century World, →	
4 **Stories** (6 titles), → (6 titles), **Stories** →						
Stage 6 **Owls** Storybooks (6 titles), **Woodpeckers Anthologies** Ten Big Fat Men, The Boy and the Tiger,	More Owls Storybooks (6 titles), **Robins** - The Dump, **More Robins** - Max Makes Breakfast,					
← **Stage 7** **Owls Storybooks** (4 titles) **More Owls Storybooks** (6 titles) **Woodpeckers Anthologies** Jill's New Bike, Wiz and Blot, →						
Robins The Old Vase, William and the Dog, **More Robins** Mum's New Car, The Long Journey,		← **Conkers Poetry** (10 titles), →				
Robins The Emergency, Kate and the Shop,	**Stage 8** **Magpies Storybooks** (6 titles),	**More Robins** The Surprise, William's Mistake,				

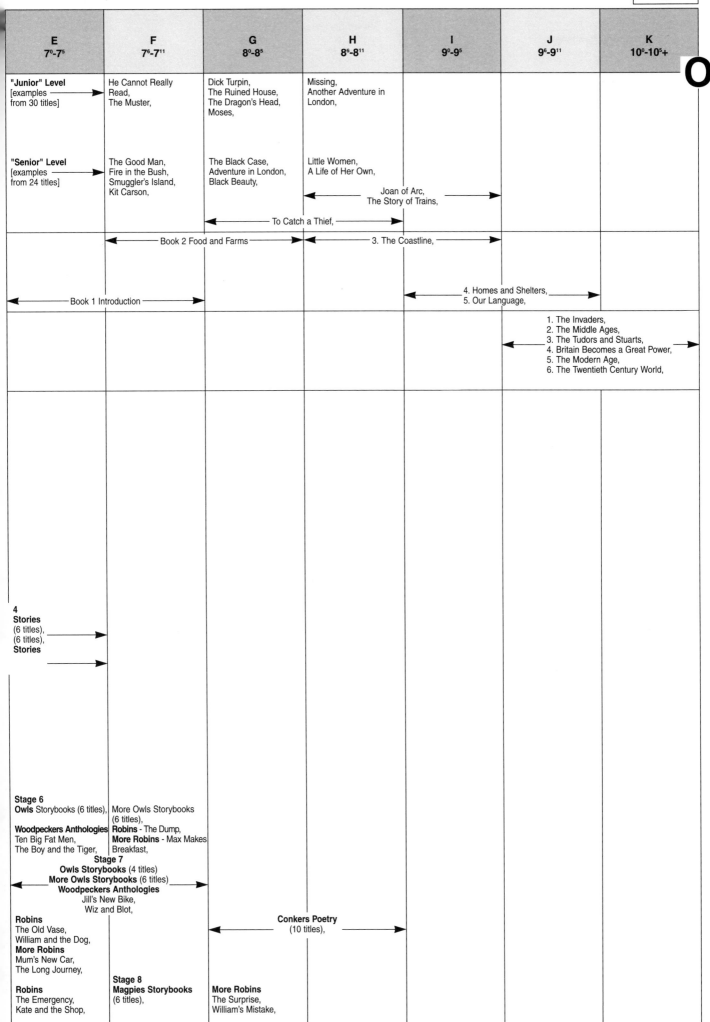

Title and Publisher	PHASE*	INTEREST AGE	Reading Level A 5^0-5^5	B 5^6-5^{11}	C 6^0-6^5	D 6^6-6^{11}
O						
Oxford Reading Tree (Continued) Oxford University Press (T, S, AU, V, IT, RR)	P	5 - 7+				
Oxford Junior Readers Oxford University Press	P/S	7 - 12			**New Stories** (previously Green series) ◄—— Books 1 —— **True Stories** (previously Orange) **Myths and Legends** (Red) **Stories from History** (Yellow)	
Oxford Myths and Legends (O/P) Oxford University Press	P/S	10 - 14+				
Oxford Progressive English Readers Oxford University Press	S	13 - 16+				
P						
Pathways Collins (T, S, AU, IT, RR)	P	4 - 8		◄—— **Stage 1** **Set A** (6 books) **Set B** (6 books)	**Set C** (6 books) **Set D** (6 books) ——►	◄—— **Stage** **Set A** **Set B** **Set C** **Set D**

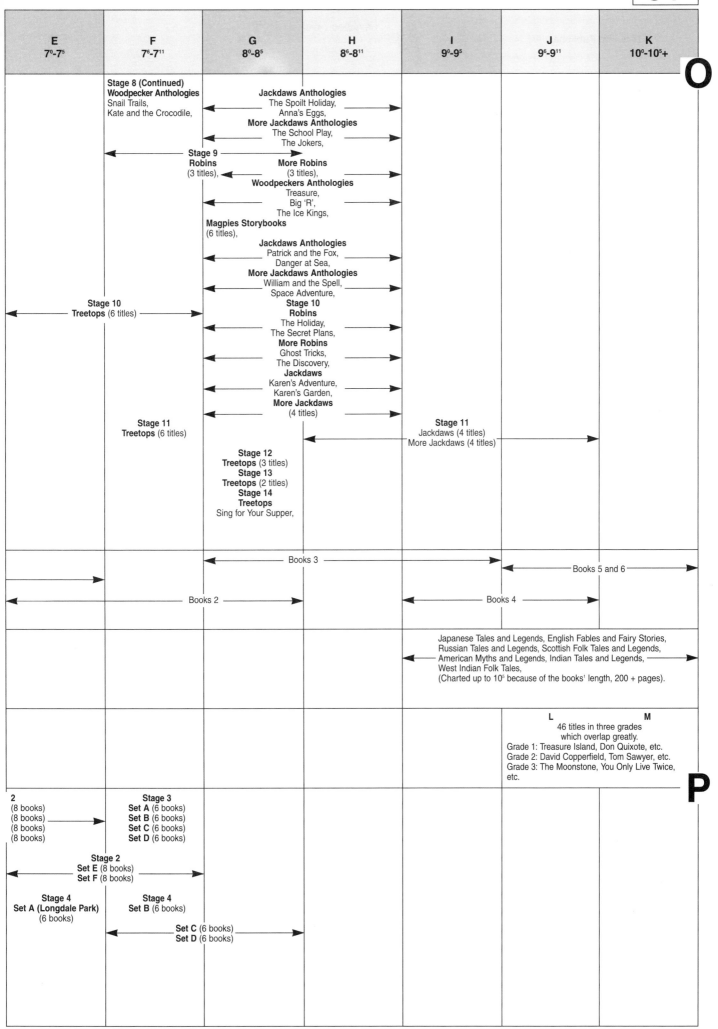

E 7^{0}-7^{5}	F 7^{6}-7^{11}	G 8^{0}-8^{5}	H 8^{6}-8^{11}	I 9^{0}-9^{5}	J 9^{6}-9^{11}	K 10^{0}-10^{5}+
O						
← **Stage 10** **Treetops** (6 titles) →	**Stage 8 (Continued)** **Woodpecker Anthologies** Snail Trails, Kate and the Crocodile, ← **Stage 9** → **Robins** (3 titles), **Stage 11** **Treetops** (6 titles)	← **Jackdaws Anthologies** The Spoilt Holiday, Anna's Eggs, → ← **More Jackdaws Anthologies** The School Play, The Jokers, → ← **More Robins** (3 titles), → ← **Woodpeckers Anthologies** Treasure, Big 'R', The Ice Kings, → **Magpies Storybooks** (6 titles), ← **Jackdaws Anthologies** Patrick and the Fox, Danger at Sea, → ← **More Jackdaws Anthologies** William and the Spell, Space Adventure, → ← **Stage 10** **Robins** The Holiday, The Secret Plans, → ← **More Robins** Ghost Tricks, The Discovery, → ← **Jackdaws** Karen's Adventure, Karen's Garden, → ← **More Jackdaws** (4 titles) → **Stage 12** **Treetops** (3 titles) **Stage 13** **Treetops** (2 titles) **Stage 14** **Treetops** Sing for Your Supper,		← **Stage 11** Jackdaws (4 titles) More Jackdaws (4 titles) →		
→ ← Books 2 →		← Books 3 →		← Books 4 →	← Books 5 and 6 →	
				← Japanese Tales and Legends, English Fables and Fairy Stories, Russian Tales and Legends, Scottish Folk Tales and Legends, American Myths and Legends, Indian Tales and Legends, West Indian Folk Tales, (Charted up to 10^{5} because of the books' length, 200 + pages). →		
					L **M** 46 titles in three grades which overlap greatly. Grade 1: Treasure Island, Don Quixote, etc. Grade 2: David Copperfield, Tom Sawyer, etc. Grade 3: The Moonstone, You Only Live Twice, etc.	
P						
2 (8 books) (8 books) → (8 books) (8 books) ← **Stage 2** **Set E** (8 books) **Set F** (8 books) → **Stage 4** **Set A (Longdale Park)** (6 books)	**Stage 3** **Set A** (6 books) **Set B** (6 books) **Set C** (6 books) **Set D** (6 books) **Stage 4** **Set B** (6 books) ← **Set C** (6 books) **Set D** (6 books) →					

P

Title and Publisher	PHASE*	INTEREST AGE	Reading Level A 5^{0}-5^{5}	B 5^{6}-5^{11}	C 6^{0}-6^{5}	D 6^{6}-6^{11}
Patter of Poems (O/P) Ginn	P	5 - 7			The Bird Table, Little Piggy-wig, Pitter Patter,	The Chickens, Cats,
Paul Groves Bookshelf Longman	S	11 - 15				
People of the Bible (O/P) Watts	P	7 - 11				
People of the World Wayland	P/S	7 - 12				
People Who Have Helped the World (HI-LO Books) (O/P) LDA	P/S	10 - 15				
Phonic Builders (O/P) Nelson	P/S	9 - 15				
Picture Library Watts	P/S	8 - 12				
Picture Lives (O/P) Watts	P/S	8 - 13				
Picturemacs (O/P) Macmillan	P	5 - 10	Paddy's Night Out, The Midnight Adventures of Kelly,	Dot and Esmeralda, Magical Changes,	One Bear Alone,	Peace at Last, Whatever Next?,
Piglet Books Methuen	P	6 - 10				

E 7^{0}-7^{5}	F 7^{6}-7^{11}	G 8^{0}-8^{5}	H 8^{6}-8^{11}	I 9^{0}-9^{5}	J 9^{6}-9^{11}	K 10^{0}-10^{5}+
		Sue's Diary, Haunted Hallowe'en,	Jack May's Secret, Tufton's Bombshell, Operation Clean-up, The Spy Who Had to Die, Six Silly Plays, Eight Even Sillier Plays,		By the Skin of His Teeth, Karen's Fun Run, Scoop of Plays,	Zany Sketches, Scoop of Stories, Plays of Evil and Suspense,
		← Miracles of the Sea (O/P), David and Goliath, Noah and His Ark (O/P), Abraham and Isaac, The Prodigal Son, Ruth's Story, Samson, The First Easter (O/P), Moses and the Plagues, The Good Samaritan, Moses Leads His People, Adam and Eve, King David, Jesus the Healer, Jesus and John the Baptist, Jesus Begins His Work, Joseph and the Dream Teller, Joseph the Long Lost Brother, The Trials of Daniel, St. Peter and St. Paul, →				
		← Aborigines, Kalahari Bushmen, Inuit, Maoris, Plains Indians, Zulus, →				
			← Mother Teresa, Bob Geldof, Marie Curie, Father Damien, Martin Luther King, Mahatma Gandhi, →			
1. Send for the Police, 2. The Summer Fair,	3. Up the River, 4. What a Week!,	5. Someone New, 8. Face to Face, 9. Adventure Playground, ← 6. A Far-off Place, 7. Winning and Losing, 10. Kindness Pays, →				
				← Space Shuttle, Computers, Motor Cycles, Racing Cars, TV and Video, Helicopters, Airlines, Trucks, Ships, etc. →		
			← The Picture Life of the Queen, Winners in Gymnastics, Winners on Ice, Winners on the Tennis Court, →			
← Donkey's Dreadful Day, On the Way Home, → Pig Pig Rides, Pig Pig Grows Up,	My Cat, ← The Mice Next Door, Mr. and Mrs. Pigs' Night Out, →		Trick a Tracker, Bringing the Rain ...,	The Story of Holly, The Hat, The King's Flower, Hugo and the Ministry...,		
	← 16 titles (adaptations of A. A. Milne's Stories), Winnie the Pooh and Some Bees, Pooh Goes Visiting, Eeyore Has a Birthday, Kanga and Baby Roo Come to the Forest, etc. →					

P

Title and Publisher	PHASE*	INTEREST AGE	Reading Level A 5^0-5^5	B 5^6-5^{11}	C 6^0-6^5	D 6^6-6^{11}
Pirate Reading Scheme, The Nelson	P	5 - 11	**Pirate Pre-readers** (Level 1) 6 titles The Red Pirate, etc.	**Griffin Pirate Stories** (Level 2) 1. The Three Pirates, 2. The Blue Pirate Sails, **Little Dragons** 1. The Sea-Dragon, 2. The Sea Witch, 3. The Princess of the Mer-People, 4. The Red Dragon, 5. The Little Blue Sea Horse, 6. The Golden Tree, Pirate I Spy Book, **Dramatic Readers** 1, 2	3. Roderick the Red, **Dragon Pirate Stories** A1. Dragon's Gold O/P A2. Islands of the Sunset, A3. The Princess who Wanted the Moon, A4. The Three Witches O/P A5. The Magic Whistle, 3, 4	4. Gregory the Green, 5. The 6. The Three Pirates Meet, 5, 6 and 7
Pitchers (O/P) Nelson	P/S	8 - 13				
Playreaders (O/P) Nelson	P/S	7 - 11				
PM Animal Books (O/P) Nelson	P	6 - 10			**Set 1** Guinea Pigs, Horses, Goldfish, Cats, Dogs, Mice, Budgies, Hens, **Set 2** Rabbits, Hares, Goats, Hedgehogs, Ducks, Pigeons, Possums, Seals,	
Pole Star Books (O/P) Cambridge University Press	P/S	7 - 12				
Primary Headwork Oxford University Press *[See also English Headwork and Headwork Stories, Headwork Reading]*	P/S	10 - 13				
Puddle Lane Ladybird (RR)	P	4 - 7+	**Stage 1:** Tim Catchamouse, The Magic Box, Tim Turns Green, etc.	**Stage 2:** Tessa in Puddle Lane, The Gruffle, The Tidy Bird, Mr. Grimble Grumbles, Magic Balloons, etc.	**Stage 3:** The Magic Dust, Magic at Midnight, Hickory Mouse, etc.	**Stage 4:** The Sandalwood Girl, When the Clock Struck On the Way to the Blue

Q

Title and Publisher	PHASE*	INTEREST AGE	A	B	C	D
Quests Longman	S	11 - 16				

P

E 7^{0}-7^{5}	F 7^{6}-7^{11}	G 8^{0}-8^{5}	H 8^{6}-8^{11}	I 9^{0}-9^{5}	J 9^{6}-9^{11}	K 10^{0}-10^{5}+
7. The Griffin, Storm, → 8. On the Island, B1. Greg and the Black Pirates, B2. A Dragon in the Wood, B3. The Three Princes, B4. Snip and the Dragon's Skin, B5. The Hollow Mountain, 8, 9 and 10 →	9. The Mirror the Candle and the Flute, C1. Ben and the People of the Bells, C2. The Country of the Red Birds, C3. The Kingdom of the Day, C4. The Mer-King's Son, C5. The White Wolf,	10. The Fight with the Black Pirates, 11. The Island of the Mer-People, ← Books 13 - 20 → (Level 3) 13. Pirate and the Mer-King 14. The Black Pirates and the Silver Net, etc. D1. The Sea Horses of the Far Islands, D2. The Ice King's Daughter, D3. The Horses of the North Wind, D4. The Pirates in the Dark Night, D5. The People of the Mist,	12. Acrooacree,			
			Gruff Treatment, The Red-Spotted Reindeer, Gold in the Garden Shed, Mr. Duckbody Superstar, The Chocolate Bar Burglar, The Runaway Reptiles, ←→			
		Set 1 Bandybones, Max and the Moon Monsters, Ben's Hens, The Toymaker's Birthday, Joey's New Smile, Little Sister, ←→		**Set 2** King Chubb and the Dragon, Litterbugs, Wild in the City, Voyage of Spaceship Fireball, Wiseman's Paradise, The Hare and the Tortoise, ←→		
			Animals Sets 1 - 6 - 24 titles: The Hare, The Hedgehog, The Rhinoceros, The Kingfisher, etc. ←→ **How People Live** Set 1 - Pygmies Move Camp, Hopi Rain Dance, Hunter in Greenland, Following the Reindeer, ←→ Set 2- Yam Festival, Jamaican Day, Amul Dairy, Wedding in Laos, ←→			
		1. The Claxton Gang, 2. More About the Claxton Gang,				
Stage 5: The Magician's Raindrops, A Dragon in the Mountains, Fire in the Grass, Thirteen, The Silver River, Mountains,						
						10 titles including: Lesley's Life, Skull Island, etc.

Q

Title and Publisher	PHASE*	INTEREST AGE	Reading Level A 5^0-5^5	B 5^6-5^{11}	C 6^0-6^5	D 6^6-6^{11}
Q						
Quest Books (O/P) Chambers	P/S	8 - 12				
Quest Game Books Oxford University Press	P/S	10 - 15				
Quizzer Books Mills and Boon	S	11 - 16				
R						
R & D (O/P) Nelson *[This is a comprehensive language scheme of which only the Story and Information Books are tabled here.]*	P	8 - 11				
Read Along Library Cambridge University Press (RR)	P	5 - 7			**Read Along Stories** Set 1, 6 titles: The Hungry Snake, Fresh Fish…, Set 2, 8 titles: The Robber Rat, Dirty Dan, Cat's Cake, Set 3, 5 titles: An Orange for the Baby, The Magic Vase, Set 4, 6 titles: The King Who Couldn't Kick, Snakes and	
	S	13 - 16+		**Read Along Rhymes** Dreadful Dragons, Hugh's Hiccups, Tim the Terrible Tiger, The Great Jam Robbery, Edwina the Explorer, Rita the Robber…,		
Read Around Hodder and Stoughton	P	8 - 11				
Read On Stanley Thornes (T, S, AU)	P/S	7 - 13				**Level 1 (Lilac):** Mark's Bike, The Den, A Burger in a Bun, Tom's Cap, Chocolate Milk Shake, The Balloon Race,

E 7^0-7^5	F 7^6-7^{11}	G 8^0-8^5	H 8^6-8^{11}	I 9^0-9^5	J 9^6-9^{11}	K 10^0-10^5+
			How Life Goes On The Frog, The Butterfly, The Duck, The Bee and the Cherry Tree, The Dolphin, The Salmon, The Roe Deer, **Tales from History** The Egg of Christopher Columbus, The Flying Balloon, The First Train, Diogenes and His Lantern, The Theft of the Mona Lisa, The Geese that Saved Rome, **Where Do Things Come From?** 7 titles **History Makers** 3 titles **Famous Cities** 3 titles			
			Pack 1 Kern the Strong, **Pack 2** Oss the Quick,			
						18 titles including: Flight, World, Mountains, People, Animals, Inventors, etc.
Level 1 Story: The Ginger Coloured Dragon, The Magic Ball, The Cabbage, Madame Zelda, Ander's Cap, What's Wrong with Lena? Information: Sun and Moon, Strange Plants, Town Fox, Records and Record Breakers, Guide Dogs,		**Level 2** Story: Harlem Globetrotters, Competitions and Ponies, The Visitors, Double Trouble, A Cry in the Night, Seal Island, Info: Chinese Customs…, The Mary Rose, Ghosts…, People and Computers, Red Deer,	**Level 3** Story: Happy Birthday, The Horse Fancier, Petticoat Smuggler, Two of a Kind, Paper Boys, The Memory Marvel, Rosalie, Info: Making a TV Programme, Dolphins, Women Explorers, The Little Hills of South India, Adventure Sports,		**Level 4** Story: The Discovery, Monkey See Monkey Do, A Path to Danger, Storm Boy, Winning all the Way, The Witness, Winston and the Robot Report, Info: Akbar…, Animals in Danger, Power from Water, Spies and Spying, Starting Life,	
The Mischievous Monkey, etc. Ant's Apple, etc. The Strange Umbrella, etc. Ladders, Peter's Pink Panda, etc.						
		Read Around, Read Around 2				
Level 2 (Red): Hello Rambo, Basketball, The Dinosaur Book, Come on, Park Road!, All About Dinosaurs, Mimi and the Dinosaur, **Level 3 (Blue):** The Map, The Shopping Trip, It's So Hot!, Tom's Sweets, Making Maps, The Dark House,	**Level 4 (Orange):** Gone Fishing, Home Sweet Home, Mark and Millie Reed, Ziggy Has a Holiday, Food Facts, A Surprise for Jip,	**Level 5 (Purple):** The Pet Show, On a Diet, The School Trip, You Can Do It!, Tatton Hall, The Ghost of Tatton Hall,	**Level 6 (Green):** The Park Road Clothes Show, We are Detectives, Sam's Detectives, The Pizza Shop, The Detective's Handbook, Catilla and the Prize Cat,			

Title and Publisher	PHASE*	INTEREST AGE	Reading Level A 5^{0}-5^{5}	B 5^{6}-5^{11}	C 6^{0}-6^{5}	D 6^{6}-6^{11}
R						
Readaway (O/P) Nelson	P	5 - 8	**Pack 1:** Red Jelly, Black, Colour In, What Is This?,	**Pack 2:** Make Something, Paul's Birthday, Samson the Rabbit, Look Out,	**Pack 3:** Big Cat Little Cat, Porridge, Tim's Bike, Where Is Coconut?,	**Pack 4:** Tree Talk, Samson Is Sick, The Ghost House, Because,
Reading Round (O/P) Nelson	P	5 - 8			← 8 titles: Reading Round the House, ... the Garden, ... the Town, ... the School, ... the Park, etc. →	
Reading 360, New Version Ginn (T, S, RR)	P	4 - 12	**Readers** **Level 1:** Look, Here, Help, Home, Digger, A New Home,	**Level 2:** Liz and Digger, Can We Help, I Can Hide, Can You?, Come for a Ride, Ben and the Duck,		**Level 3:** Don't Run Away, Digger at School, A Duck is a Duck, Horses, Picnic for Tortoise, Lost and Found, **Level 4:** At the Zoo, Helicopters, Animal Tales,
			Little Books **Level 1:** **Set 1** (6 books), **Set 2** (6 books), **Set 3** (6 books), **Non-fiction** (6 books),	← **Level 2:** **Set 1** (6 books), **Set 2** (6 books), **Set 3** (6 books), **Non-fiction** (6 books), →		**Level 3:** **Set 1** (6 books), **Set 2** (6 books), **Set 3** (6 books), **Non-fiction** (6 books),

E 7^0-7^5	F 7^6-7^{11}	G 8^0-8^5	H 8^6-8^{11}	I 9^0-9^5	J 9^6-9^{11}	K 10^0-10^5+
Pack 5: What Animal Is This?, Sticks and Bones, The Picnic, The Rocket Trip,	**Pack 6:** A Recipe Book, Flop Has Died, The Old House, The Tadpole,					
	Level 5: Animal Tracks, In the Town, Dogs and Whistles, All for Fun, Old Tales, Faraway Tales,	**Level 6:** Let's Be Friends, Balloons, City Life, Snowy Days, Time to Smile, Machines, Tales We Like,				
Level 4: What a Surprise!, Once Upon a Time, Animal Friends,						
Level 4: **Set 1** (6 titles), **Set 2** (6 titles), **Set 3** (6 titles), **Non-fiction** (6 titles),	**Level 5:** **Set 1** (6 titles), **Set 2** (6 titles), **Set 3** (6 titles), **Non-fiction** (6 titles),					
	Pocket Books **Level 5** (4 books),					
	Level 6: **Set 1** (4 books), **Set 3** (4 books),	**Set 2** (4 books), **Set 4** (4 books),				
		Readers **Level 7:** Pet Tales, Animals, Transport, Places to Visit, Around the World, Long Ago and Far Away,				
			Level 8: Messages, Through the Year, Magical Tales,			
				Festivals, In Our Family, Moonshine,		
					Level 9: Meet the Family, Stuff and Nonsense, The Sea, Just for Fun, The Pirate Bed (novel),	
					Level 10: A School Bag, Animal Lore, Children in History, Another Time, Another Place, Run for It! (novel),	
						Level 11: I Spy Sci-fi, Don't Look Now…, Sports and Hobbies, Looking After Auntie,
		Pocket Books **Level 7:** **Set 1** (4 books), **Set 2** (4 books), **Set 3** (4 books), **Set 4** (4 books),		**Level 9:** **Set 1** (4 books), **Set 2** (4 books),		**Levels 10, 11 and 12** **2 Sets** of 4 books at each Level,
		Level 8: **Set 1** (4 books), **Set 2** (4 books), **Set 3** (4 books),				

R

Title and Publisher	PHASE*	INTEREST AGE	Reading Level A 5^0-5^5	B 5^6-5^{11}	C 6^0-6^5	D 6^6-6^{11}
Reading 360, Original Series Ginn (T, S)	P/S	5 - 12	**Readers** **Level 1:** Look, Here's Help, Home, Lad, Ben,	**Level 2:** Ben and Lad, Can We Help?, I Can Hide, Come for a Ride, Ben and Shorty,		**Level 3:** The Park, The Tortoise, I Can Read, Horses, A Picnic for Tortoise, Where Are You Going?, **Level 4:** At the Zoo, Helicopters, A Book for Kay,
			Magic Circle Books **Level 1:** We Need a Bigger Zoo, Walk Robot Walk, The Bumbershot,		**Level 2:** Ride, Ride, Ride, Hide, The Park, The Park,	**Level 3:** Stop! Look, Cat, Back in the Park..., Where is Zip?, Look with May Ling, **Level 4:** Do You See a Mouse?, "What Is It?" said Dog, In the Zoo,
			Little Books **Level 1:** 12 titles: Frog Spell, Is This My Home?, Butterfly, etc.	**Level 2:** Can I Play?, Look Like Me,	**Level 2:** Up We Go, Hide, Can You See Me?, Come and Play with Me, etc.	**Level 3:** 12 titles: Reindeer, Play a Play, Guess What a Cat Found, Going to the Shops, etc.

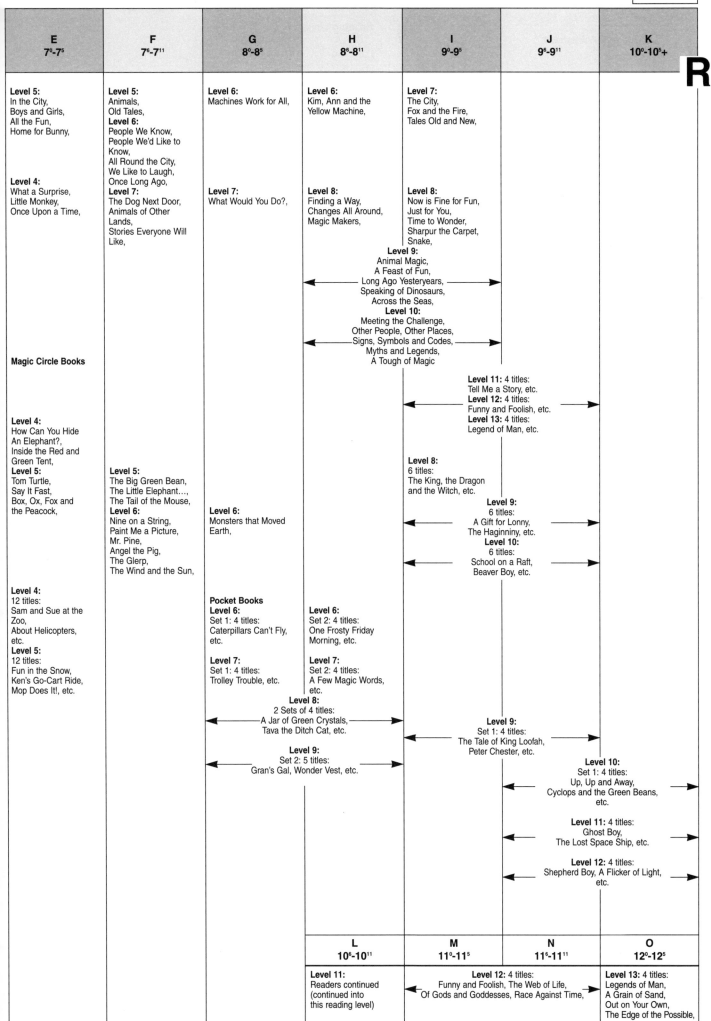

<table>
<tr><th>E
7^{0}-7^{5}</th><th>F
7^{6}-7^{11}</th><th>G
8^{0}-8^{5}</th><th>H
8^{6}-8^{11}</th><th>I
9^{0}-9^{5}</th><th>J
9^{6}-9^{11}</th><th>K
10^{0}-10^{5}+</th></tr>
<tr><td>Level 5:
In the City,
Boys and Girls,
All the Fun,
Home for Bunny,</td><td>Level 5:
Animals,
Old Tales,
Level 6:
People We Know,
People We'd Like to Know,
All Round the City,
We Like to Laugh,
Once Long Ago,</td><td>Level 6:
Machines Work for All,</td><td>Level 6:
Kim, Ann and the Yellow Machine,</td><td>Level 7:
The City,
Fox and the Fire,
Tales Old and New,</td><td></td><td></td></tr>
<tr><td>Level 4:
What a Surprise,
Little Monkey,
Once Upon a Time,</td><td>Level 7:
The Dog Next Door,
Animals of Other Lands,
Stories Everyone Will Like,</td><td>Level 7:
What Would You Do?,</td><td>Level 8:
Finding a Way,
Changes All Around,
Magic Makers,</td><td>Level 8:
Now is Fine for Fun,
Just for You,
Time to Wonder,
Sharpur the Carpet,
Snake,</td><td></td><td></td></tr>
<tr><td></td><td></td><td></td><td colspan="3">Level 9:
Animal Magic,
A Feast of Fun,
Long Ago Yesteryears,
Speaking of Dinosaurs,
Across the Seas,</td><td></td></tr>
<tr><td></td><td></td><td></td><td colspan="3">Level 10:
Meeting the Challenge,
Other People, Other Places,
Signs, Symbols and Codes,
Myths and Legends,
A Tough of Magic</td><td></td></tr>
<tr><td>Magic Circle Books</td><td></td><td></td><td></td><td colspan="3">Level 11: 4 titles:
Tell Me a Story, etc.
Level 12: 4 titles:
Funny and Foolish, etc.
Level 13: 4 titles:
Legend of Man, etc.</td></tr>
<tr><td rowspan="3">Level 4:
How Can You Hide An Elephant?,
Inside the Red and Green Tent,
Level 5:
Tom Turtle,
Say It Fast,
Box, Ox, Fox and the Peacock,</td><td rowspan="3">Level 5:
The Big Green Bean,
The Little Elephant…,
The Tail of the Mouse,
Level 6:
Nine on a String,
Paint Me a Picture,
Mr. Pine,
Angel the Pig,
The Glerp,
The Wind and the Sun,</td><td rowspan="3">Level 6:
Monsters that Moved Earth,</td><td rowspan="3"></td><td>Level 8:
6 titles:
The King, the Dragon and the Witch, etc.</td><td></td><td></td></tr>
<tr><td colspan="3">Level 9:
6 titles:
A Gift for Lonny,
The Haginniny, etc.</td></tr>
<tr><td colspan="3">Level 10:
6 titles:
School on a Raft,
Beaver Boy, etc.</td></tr>
<tr><td>Level 4:
12 titles:
Sam and Sue at the Zoo,
About Helicopters, etc.
Level 5:
12 titles:
Fun in the Snow,
Ken's Go-Cart Ride,
Mop Does It!, etc.</td><td></td><td>Pocket Books
Level 6:
Set 1: 4 titles:
Caterpillars Can't Fly, etc.

Level 7:
Set 1: 4 titles:
Trolley Trouble, etc.</td><td>Level 6:
Set 2: 4 titles:
One Frosty Friday Morning, etc.

Level 7:
Set 2: 4 titles:
A Few Magic Words, etc.</td><td></td><td></td><td></td></tr>
<tr><td></td><td></td><td colspan="2">Level 8:
2 Sets of 4 titles:
A Jar of Green Crystals,
Tava the Ditch Cat, etc.</td><td colspan="3">Level 9:
Set 1: 4 titles:
The Tale of King Loofah,
Peter Chester, etc.</td></tr>
<tr><td></td><td></td><td colspan="2">Level 9:
Set 2: 5 titles:
Gran's Gal, Wonder Vest, etc.</td><td></td><td></td><td></td></tr>
<tr><td></td><td></td><td></td><td></td><td></td><td colspan="2">Level 10:
Set 1: 4 titles:
Up, Up and Away,
Cyclops and the Green Beans, etc.

Level 11: 4 titles:
Ghost Boy,
The Lost Space Ship, etc.

Level 12: 4 titles:
Shepherd Boy, A Flicker of Light, etc.</td></tr>
<tr><td></td><td></td><td></td><th>L
10^{6}-10^{11}</th><th>M
11^{0}-11^{5}</th><th>N
11^{6}-11^{11}</th><th>O
12^{0}-12^{5}</th></tr>
<tr><td></td><td></td><td></td><td>Level 11:
Readers continued (continued into this reading level)</td><td colspan="2">Level 12: 4 titles:
Funny and Foolish, The Web of Life,
Of Gods and Goddesses, Race Against Time,</td><td>Level 13: 4 titles:
Legends of Man,
A Grain of Sand,
Out on Your Own,
The Edge of the Possible,</td></tr>
</table>

R

Title and Publisher	PHASE*	INTEREST AGE	Reading Level A 5^0-5^5	B 5^6-5^{11}	C 6^0-6^5	D 6^6-6^{11}
Reading Rigby (O/P) Blackwell	P	5 - 9	**Level 1** 12 titles	**Level 2** Scratch, Scratch, Help Mum, Play Mr. Wind, **Leapfrog** (phonics) Group 1 10 books	Red Fire, Buzz the Bee,	The Frog and the Ox, **Level 3** Ant and the Grasshopper, Wilga Witch, Last Monday, The Big T, Steam Train Day, Group 2 10 books
Reading 2000 Longman						
Reading Well Longman	P/S	8 - 12				
Read it Yourself (Series 777) Ladybird	P	5 - 7	**Level 2:** 1. Goldilocks, 2. Billy Goats Gruff, 3. Sly Fox and Red Hen, 4. The Elves and the Shoemaker, 5. Hansel and Gretel, 6. Enormous Turnip,	**Level 3:** 1. The Three Little Pigs, 2. Red Riding Hood, 3. Puss in Boots, 4. Dick Whittington, 5. Peter and the Wolf, 6. Rapunzel, **Level 4:** 1. The Gingerbread Man, 2. Jack and the Beanstalk, 3. Cinderella, 4. Snow White, 5. The Pied Piper, 6. Wizard of Oz,	**Level 5:** 1. Robinson Crusoe, 2. The Magic Stone, 3. William Tell, 4. Heidi, 5. Magic Paintbrush, 6. Ananse and the Sky God,	
Read, Write and Remember Nelson	P	6 - 9			Introductory Book, Early Books 1 - 4, Early Chasers 1 - 4	Original Main Books 1 - 8 New Books 1 - 8 Reading Success Books (5 titles)
Real Life Reading Skills Heinemann	S	14 - 18				
Real Lives: Bollywood Stars Hodder and Stoughton/ Basic Skills Agency	S	12 - 16+				
Red Lion Books (O/P) (Holt, Rinehart and Winston) Cassell	S	11 - 15				

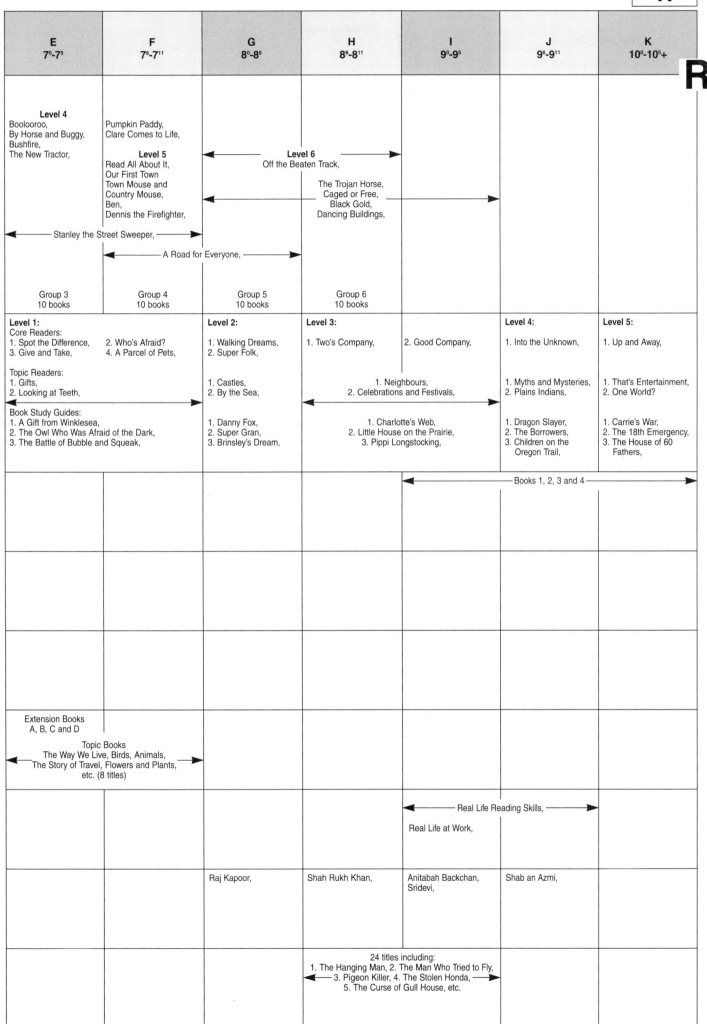

E 7^{0}-7^{5}	F 7^{6}-7^{11}	G 8^{0}-8^{5}	H 8^{6}-8^{11}	I 9^{0}-9^{5}	J 9^{6}-9^{11}	K 10^{0}-10^{5}+
Level 4 Boolooroo, By Horse and Buggy, Bushfire, The New Tractor, Stanley the Street Sweeper, Group 3 10 books	Pumpkin Paddy, Clare Comes to Life, **Level 5** Read All About It, Our First Town Town Mouse and Country Mouse, Ben, Dennis the Firefighter, A Road for Everyone, Group 4 10 books	**Level 6** Off the Beaten Track, The Trojan Horse, Caged or Free, Black Gold, Dancing Buildings, Group 5 10 books	Group 6 10 books			
Level 1: Core Readers: 1. Spot the Difference, 3. Give and Take, Topic Readers: 1. Gifts, 2. Looking at Teeth, Book Study Guides: 1. A Gift from Winklesea, 2. The Owl Who Was Afraid of the Dark, 3. The Battle of Bubble and Squeak,	2. Who's Afraid? 4. A Parcel of Pets,	**Level 2:** 1. Walking Dreams, 2. Super Folk, 1. Castles, 2. By the Sea, 1. Danny Fox, 2. Super Gran, 3. Brinsley's Dream,	**Level 3:** 1. Two's Company, 1. Neighbours, 2. Celebrations and Festivals, 1. Charlotte's Web, 2. Little House on the Prairie, 3. Pippi Longstocking,	2. Good Company,	**Level 4:** 1. Into the Unknown, 1. Myths and Mysteries, 2. Plains Indians, 1. Dragon Slayer, 2. The Borrowers, 3. Children on the Oregon Trail,	**Level 5:** 1. Up and Away, 1. That's Entertainment, 2. One World? 1. Carrie's War, 2. The 18th Emergency, 3. The House of 60 Fathers,
				Books 1, 2, 3 and 4		
Extension Books A, B, C and D Topic Books The Way We Live, Birds, Animals, The Story of Travel, Flowers and Plants, etc. (8 titles)						
				Real Life Reading Skills, Real Life at Work,		
		Raj Kapoor,	Shah Rukh Khan,	Anitabah Backchan, Sridevi,	Shab an Azmi,	
			24 titles including: 1. The Hanging Man, 2. The Man Who Tried to Fly, 3. Pigeon Killer, 4. The Stolen Honda, 5. The Curse of Gull House, etc.			

Title and Publisher	PHASE*	INTEREST AGE	Reading Level A 5^{0}-5^{5}	B 5^{6}-5^{11}	C 6^{0}-6^{5}	D 6^{6}-6^{11}
R						
Relay Readers, The Schofield and Sims	S	12 - 18				**The Red** 1. A Mad 2. What a ← 3. Pot Shots, 4. Lost and 5. One Good 6. The Final
Rescue Reading Ginn (S)	P/S	8 - 14		**Shorty the Puppy** 1. John, 2. The Puppy, 3. Bad Puppy!, 4. Good Puppy!, 5. A New Home, 6. The Dump,	**Young Shorty Books** 1. The Rescue, 2. Breakfast, 3. Mark Fox, **More Young Shorty Books** 1. The Lost Puppy, 2. Police Dog, 3. Free!, **Young Shorty Again** 1. Fire!, 2. Water,	4. Burglars!, 5. Mark Fox Again, 6. Run Over!, 4. Bad Luck, 5. The Fox Trap, 6. Dead?, 3. The Fight, 4. Vicky's House, 5. Out!,
Rhyme Readers Ginn (RR)	P	5 - 7		← Books 1 - 8: This Little Pig, Mary Had a Little Lamb, Boys and Girls ..., etc. Books 9 - 14: Old Mother Hubbard, The House that Jack Built, The Three Little Kittens, etc. →		The Queen of Hearts, The Cuckoo and the North Wind, All the Sea Were One Sea,
Rhythm and Rhyme (O/P) Ginn (RR)	P	5 - 7			I Can Squeak, Stables Are for Horses, Tomatoes and Bricks, One Sun in the Sky,	
Robot the Robot (O/P) Ginn	P	7 - 10				
Roundabouts (O/P) Nelson	P	6 - 10			← A: 4 titles A1: Willie the Soldier, etc. →	B: 4 titles B1: The Giant's
Round the World Folk Tales (O/P) Macmillan	P/S	7 - 12				
S						
Science (Series 621) (Some titles O/P) Ladybird	P/S	9 - 14				

R

E 7^0-7^5	F 7^6-7^{11}	G 8^0-8^5	H 8^6-8^{11}	I 9^0-9^5	J 9^6-9^{11}	K 10^0-10^5+
Books Scramble, Catch, Found, Turn, Score,	**The Yellow Books** 1. The Hiding Place, 2. A Near Thing, 3. The Bullfighter, 4. No Contest, 5. A Bad Break, 6. Canal Jack,		**The Green Books** 1. A Fair Cop!, 2. Christmas Shopping, 3. Gone Fishing, 4. Home and Away, 5. Witch Hunt, 6. A Fighting Chance,		**The Blue Books** 1. Strange Meeting, 2. Pit Stop!, 3. Not a Leg to Stand On!, 4. Race Against the Tide, 5. Bringing the House Down, 6. Down Under,	
7. Aunt Norah, 8. False Alarm, 9. The Stolen Truck, 10. The Chocolate Shop,	11. Cousin Karen, 12. Won and Lost,					
7. What a Day, 8. The Snow Ghost,	9. Boy's Bone, 10. Shop Thief, 11. Karen's Bike, 12. A Real Hero,					
Rescue Stories Shorty the Hero, Shorty and Tom Rabbit,	Shorty and the Bank Robbers, Sally the Seagull,	Martin the Mouse, Brown Beauty,	**More Rescue Stories** Patrick the Parrot, Hoppy the Second, Snowball, Shorty Again, Firewater, Trouble the Fox,			
6. Blind!, 7. The Fair,		11. Karen's Cave, 12. Tin Fish,				
8. The Steam Rally, 9. Smash and Grab!, 10. Good as Gold,				**Rescue Adventures** Adventure in Jersey, Adventure Underground, Adventure on the Road, Adventure in Scotland, City Adventure, Adventure in Space,		
			6 titles: Robot the Robot, Robot and the Great Sale, etc.			
C: 4 titles C1: Samantha's New House, etc.				H: 4 titles H1: The Seven Red Dragons, etc.,	I: 4 titles I1: It is Always Dark for a Blind Man, etc.	
Socks, etc.	D: 4 titles D1: The Secret Room, etc.,	E: 4 titles E1: The Dragon of Yang-Wong, etc.	F: 4 titles F1: The Peppermint Man, etc.	G: 4 titles G1: The Adventure of the Kite, etc.	J: 4 titles J1: The Terrible Pet, etc.	
	Brown: Mr. Wolf and His Tail, The Antelope and the Turtle,		**Orange:** Uncle Bouki and the Horse, Grandfather Frost,		**Green:** Gormless Tom, The Hairy Toe, **Blue:** Smoking Star, Maui Stealer of Fire,	
		Red: Brer Annancy's Second Bite, The Tiger and the Rabbit,		**Yellow:** The Legend of the Frogs, The Wise Judge,		
		1. Magnets and Electricity, 2. Light, 3. Air, 4. Simple Mechanics, 5. Simple Chemistry, 6. Botany, 7. Zoology, 8. Weather,				

S

S

Title and Publisher	PHASE*	INTEREST AGE	Reading Level A 5^{0}-5^{5}	B 5^{6}-5^{11}	C 6^{0}-6^{5}	D 6^{6}-6^{11}
Scottish Life Stanley Thornes	P/S					
Scripture Union Bible Books (Series SU 781) Ladybird	P/S	6 - 12				
Search for the Past (O/P) Ginn	P/S	8 - 13				
Sharp Eye (Theme Books) Ginn *[There is considerably more material to Sharp Eye than is charted here]*	P	7 - 9				
Seven Silly Stories (O/P) Longman	P	5 - 8				Mr. Stupid, The Miller and His Donkey, The Foolish Tortoise, Noisy Neville,
Simple Science Black	P	5 - 7			← My Feathers, My Jumper, My Boat, My Mirror, My Balloon, My Shadow, My Cake, My Apple, My Drum, My Car, My Magnet, My Shell, →	

<table>
<tr><th>E
7^0-7^5</th><th>F
7^6-7^{11}</th><th>G
8^0-8^5</th><th>H
8^6-8^{11}</th><th>I
9^0-9^5</th><th>J
9^6-9^{11}</th><th>K
10^0-10^5+</th></tr>
<tr><td></td><td></td><td></td><td></td><td></td><td></td><td>Scottish LIfe Before 1500,
Scottish Life 1500-1750,
Scottish History,
1700 to Recent Times,</td></tr>
<tr><td></td><td></td><td colspan="2">Moses and Joshua, Samuel and Saul,
Elijah and Elisha, Daniel and Esther,
Jesus in Danger, The Easter Story,
Paul the Traveller, Paul the Prisoner,
Peter,</td><td></td><td></td><td></td></tr>
<tr><td></td><td></td><td></td><td colspan="2">Digging up the Past, Great Finds,
Ancient Animals and Plants,
Finding Ancient Things, Finding Ancient Places,
Looking After Ancient Places,</td><td></td><td></td></tr>
<tr><td colspan="2">**Level 1:**
Theme - Myself Story Books
Gluggy Gets Sick, Gluggy's Christmas,
Gluggy the Champion

Information Books
Minnie Pink Ears, The Three Splodgies…,

Starter Book Set - 6 titles:
Myself Catalogue, All About Me, Me, I'm Myself, etc.

Theme: Home and Friends Story Book
Peter's House, The Planet of the Shapes,
Things I Can Do at Home, Your Monster Friend,
Dream House,

Theme: School Story Books
Floyd, Schooldays, Smile Clare, The Silly Table,

Information Books:
The Old School, The School Caretaker's Day,

Starter Book Set
About My School, Identikit School,
Things I Can Do at School, School Catalogue,
Superspy Goes to School, The Day the Dinosaur…,
Super School,</td><td>Home and Friends
Catalogue, Rat-a-Tat
Who Is That?;</td><td></td><td></td><td></td><td></td></tr>
<tr><td colspan="3">**Level 2: My World** (provisional placings)
Fish and Chips, Lucky Ring, Traffic Jam,
Busy Street, Claire's Town, My World,

Creatures
Bones and the Beast, Bones at the Pet Show,
Bones and the Monsters, Jill Has Three Pets,
Who Rolled in the Mud?, Beth's Bird Table,

Going Places
Candy Can-do Goes to Spy Island,
Candy Can-do and the King's Diamond,
Candy Can-do and the Dragon Doors,
Out with Grandad,</td><td>Pip Goes to Africa,
How We Travelled …,</td><td></td><td></td><td></td></tr>
<tr><td>The Well Diggers,
The Fox and the Stork,
Brer Rabbit and the
Honey Pot,</td><td></td><td></td><td></td><td></td><td></td><td></td></tr>
<tr><td></td><td></td><td></td><td></td><td></td><td></td><td></td></tr>
</table>

S

Title and Publisher	PHASE*	INTEREST AGE	Reading Level A 5^{0}-5^{5}	B 5^{6}-5^{11}	C 6^{0}-6^{5}	D 6^{6}-6^{11}
Skyways Collins	P/S	8 - 12+			**Level 1:** **Country Stories** Old Sally, Matilda the Mouse, The House on Sunset Hill, The Pitta Patta Birds, **Hedgehog Stories** The Igel, Spring Again, Night in the Garden, The Monster, **Information Books** In the Country, In the Garden,	**Level 2:** **Ghost Stories** The Black Dog, The Phone Box, Footprints in the Snow, Ghost Knife, **Transport Stories** The Old Aeroplane, Mr. Peddle's Pennyfarthing, The Old Car, The Old Boat, Ghost Hunters Transport Old and New,
Sound Sense (O/P) Nelson	P/S	6 - 13				1, 2 **Sound Sense Stories** 1A. Brenda's Find, B. The Airfields Mystery, C. A Story from Denmark, 2A. The Lost Boy, B. The Fisherman's Son, C. Two Grimm Tales,
Space Pilot Trilogy (HI-LO Books) LDA	P/S	9 - 16				
Spirals Stanley Thomas	S	12 - 16				
Spooked! Hodder and Stoughton/ Basic Skills Agency	S	13 - 16+				
Sports Bag Cambridge University Press	P/S	8 - 12				

E 7^{0}-7^{5}	F 7^{6}-7^{11}	G 8^{0}-8^{5}	H 8^{6}-8^{11}	I 9^{0}-9^{5}	J 9^{6}-9^{11}	K 10^{0}-10^{5}+
Level 3: **Robot Stories** Fred and the Robot, Big Max and the Oil Rig, Big Max and the Satellite, Big Max Goes to the Moon, **Dracula Stories** Count Dracula and the Ghost, ...and the Monster, ...and theVictim, ...Meets His Match, Bungling Burglars, Pop Star Returns, 007½ and the Homework Mystery, Rundown on Robots, Spine Chiller	**Level 4:** **Family Stories** Tim, Dad, Mum, Gran, **Detective Stories** Nick Dick at the Races, Nick Dick and Who Strangled Lord Howard, Nick Dick and the Drug Smugglers, Nick Dick and the Gorilla, ← **Level 7:** Alice Lost, Crabapple Wood, Kidnapped, Great Gran, Tina Top of the Pops, → Fishy Facts, Detectives,	**Level 5:** **Sports Stories** Rosie's Race, Billy's Bike, Tejender's Target, Dad's First Swim, **Knights and Castles Stories** First Meeting, War Horse, Christmas, The Dragon, Sport, Knights and Castles,	**Level 6:** **Entertainment Stories** The Buskers, Filming, Errol and His Group, The Disco, **Magic Stories** The Ramshackle Shoe, The MOT Test, Trip to the Zoo, Competition Time, Entertainment, Magic,	Being Silly,		Communications,
3, 4 3A. A Bible Story, B. Three Greek Myths, C. Scott's Last Journey, 4A. The School Camp, B. Saxon and Norse Tales, C. The Mystery of the Marsh,	5, 5A. Two More Grimm Tales, B. The Cornish Witch, C. The Black Treasure,	6, 7	8	← 9 →	← 10 →	
				← Set of 3 Books →		
← The Actor, The Austin Seven, The Ring, A Game of Life and Death, Loves Me, Maggot, → **Spiral Plays** An Earwig in the Ear, Package Holiday, Hard Times, Cheer and Groan, The Bungle Gang Strikes Again,	Pentag, No Rent to Pay, The Third Climber, Not that I'm Work-shy, Beware of the Morris Minor, Tell Me Where it Hurts, When I Count to Three, Punchlines, The End of the Line, Making a Splash, Murder at Mucklebury Manor, Taking the Plunge,	Eye of Evil, Summer of the Werewolf, The Dark Shadow, Dollars in the Dust, Snake, Jimmy Rocket, Doctor Comes to the Circus, The Witch Princess, Inside and Out, Crash in the Jungle, Nightmare Lake, Fame and Fortune, The Good, the Bad and the Bungle, Time Loop, Computer Killer, No Entry, Hanging by a Fred,				
Hooked!, Murder in Mind, Coming Home,	A Lucky Charm,					
						(3 books, 2 stories in each) Girl in Goal and Catches Win Matches, etc.

S

Title and Publisher	PHASE*	INTEREST AGE	Reading Level A 5^{0}-5^{5}	B 5^{6}-5^{11}	C 6^{0}-6^{5}	D 6^{6}-6^{11}
Sprint Books Nelson	S	13 - 16+				
Squirrels (O/P) Longman	P/S	10 - 15				
Stories for Today (O/P) Heinemann	S	13 - 16+				
Starpol Ginn	P/S	8 - 14+				
Start with Rhymes Ginn (RR)	P	5 - 7		◄ Books 1 - 6: Humpty Dumpty, Jack and Jill, Bedtime, etc. Books 7 - 12: Little Miss Muffet, One Two Buckle My Shoe, In a Dark Wood, etc. ►		
Star/Shooting Stars (O/P) Macmillan	P	5 - 9	**Star:** Blue: The Grand Old Duke, Jack and Jill, The Crooked Man, Kangaroo's Umbrella, Bad Cat, **Shooting Stars** *[Shooting Stars are all a little more advanced and often overlap the next column.]*	Green: Tom Tom the Piper's Son, Sing a Song of Sixpence, Mary Had a Little Lamb, The Puddle, My Hat, Green: Rain, At the Tower, Tiger T-Shirt, The Big Tail, Cat Rhymes,	Purple: The Queen of Hearts, I Saw a Ship A-Sailing, Fat Fox, The Birthday Ball, The Gigantic Turnip, Purple: Twelve Little Girls, Twelve Little Boys, Sarah's T-Shirt, Dan the Dinosaur, The Big Fib,	Red: Old Mother Hubbard, Two Long Rhymes, Lazy Jack, The Red Flowers, Kili the Curious Weka, Red: Twelve Rhymes, The Twelve Days of Christmas, The Mop…, Jumping Jo…, Crab Apples,
Stopwatch Black	P	6 - 11				
Storyboards (O/P) Ginn	P	7 - 9				The Red Lion, The Elephant's Nest, The Fox and Hounds,

S

E 7^{0}-7^{5}	F 7^{6}-7^{11}	G 8^{0}-8^{5}	H 8^{6}-8^{11}	I 9^{0}-9^{5}	J 9^{6}-9^{11}	K 10^{0}-10^{5}+
	Set 1: Where There's a Will, Margret Is Troubled, Scare for Janet, Wave of Excitement, **Set 2:** Jimmy Grows Up, One of the Boys, Who Cares?, A Brush with the Law, **Set 3:** A Matter of Opinion, Collision Course, Strange Encounter, Narrow Escape,					
	Stage 1 ← Black Beauty, King Arthur, etc. →	**Stage 2** The Secret Garden, ← The Prince and the Pauper, etc. →	**Stage 3** ← Dracula, The Blue Lagoon, etc. →	**Stage 4** ← Jane Eyre, White Fang, etc. →	**Stage 5** ← Lord Jim, Allen Quartermain, etc. →	
First Series 1. Ron's Flight, 2. Ginger and Sharon, 3. Frank's Fire, 4. Linda's Journey,	5. Joe and Carol, 6. Diane's Sister, **Second Series** 7. Paul, 9. Naomi, 10. June's Work, 11. Rescue at Night,	8. Donovan, 12. The Big Game,				
	Hunter Three Story Books (6 titles)	**Hunter Four Story Books** (6 titles) **Pocket Books** (4 titles)	**1 - 8 Story Books** The New Man, Raiders on Zeta, ← The Ants, Mayday Call, → The Spider, The Truggs,	Old Moggy, Ghost of Zol,		
Yellow: Twenty Rhymes, Almond Blossom, The Emperor's New Clothes, The Witch's Daughter, Koala's Tail,						
27 titles including: Apple Tree, Bird's Nest, Broad Bean, Bumblebee, Chicken and Egg, Newt, etc.						
The Blinking Owl, The Dusty Miller, The Whistling Pig,						

Title and Publisher	PHASE*	INTEREST AGE	Reading Level A 5^0-5^5	B 5^6-5^{11}	C 6^0-6^5	D 6^6-6^{11}
S **Story Chest** (Nelson) Kingscourt Publishing (T, S, AU, RR)	P	5 - 10	**Stage 1** Big book Sets, Get Ready Sets A and B, Small Read Together, Ready-Set-Go Sets A-D, ◄— The Ready-Set-Go books —►	◄— **Stage 3** Let Me In, Sun Smile, Storybooks (4), —► **Stage 2** Help Me, Roly Poly, The Pirates, Wet Grass, The Kick-a-Lot Shoes,	**Stage 4** Just Like Me, Fast and Funny, Storybooks (4), **Bridges** **Set A** The School Concert, The Fancy Dress Parade, You Might Fall, etc. **Set B** Splashing, Blue Lollipops, Colours of the Week, etc., **Set C** Making Music, Making Potato Heads, Making Weather Poems, etc.	**Stage 6** ◄— Fiddle-dee-dee, Story Books **Stage 5** Well I Never, Sing to the Moon, Storybooks (4) **Stepping Stones** (non-fiction) **Set A** A Matchbox Collection, Collecting Shapes, Collecting Badges, Collecting Leaves, The Public Library, The Natural History Museum, **Set B** Hannah, Zunid, Paul and Lucy, Emil, Daisy, Elaine,
Story Corner (O/P) Nelson	P	5 - 9			**Level 1** What's the Time, Mr. Wolf?, Who's the Biggest?, **Level 3** Animal Noises,	**Level 1** Sinka's New Coat, The Elephant Ride, A Fishy Tale, Why Do Elephants Wear Hats?, Leaves, Spooky Sounds, I Can't Find My Glasses, How Far Can You Jump, One Dark, Dark Night, There Was a Crooked Man, Is There Room for Me?, Five Little Monkeys, At Weekends, Shopping, Five Little Chickens, **Level 2** Amy, Claire and the Legs, John, the Track Spotter, The Exploding Frog, The Pedlar, The Lion and the Mouse, The Old Woman and Her Pig, Black Witch, Black Witch, Over in the Meadow, Aunt Fig Sells Her Pig, Keys, Sharing Food,

E 7^{0}-7^{5}	F 7^{6}-7^{11}	G 8^{0}-8^{5}	H 8^{6}-8^{11}	I 9^{0}-9^{5}	J 9^{6}-9^{11}	K 10^{0}-10^{5}+
Cooking Pot, → (4)	← **Stage 7** More! More! More! Tiddalik, Storybooks (4) →	**Stage 8** Fairy Tales, Green Grobblop at the Seaside, Don't Be Silly, Nandini, Inside Story 1, etc., ← **Selection Box** Greased Lightning Grobblop, Mr. Grump and Fleabag, Scraggs Flowers, The Burglar, Gus, Boot Sale, Nessy, Wolf, Mrs. Peppers, →	**Stage 9** Beyond the Horizon, Wondermouse, Inside Story 2, Oh Really, How Interesting, A Prince and a Fish,	**Stage 10** Around the World, Mags and Other Stories, Inside Story 3, The Little Tree, Be Quiet When I'm Talking, Myth and Magic, etc. Living Legends, A Test of Truth, etc., Pick and Mix, Harold and Huwi, The Floating World,	← **Stages 11 - 19** Many titles → Morgan Price, Investigates, - Coal, Gas, Oil, Beowolf, The Chasm, The Three Kings,	**Stage 20** Remi versus the Robbies, The Gibleteers, etc. Images from History, The Great Ox of Verbena, Hattie in a Hurry, Tolly on Tuesday, A Question of Honour, Friends and Neighbours, The Riotous Return…, Under the Almond Tree, More Stories Under the Almond Tree, Paths to Glory, For Love and Honour, The End of an Era, Jungle at Home, Top Twenty, Smile Please, King Arthur's, Shadow of the Serpent, Children of the Moon,
Level 3 Moggy's Hop, Henry's Ears,	**Level 3** Waria and the Pocket,	**Level 3** The Princess and the Poet, The Boy Who Cried Wolf, The Man Who Found Salt, **Level 4** Jelly on the Plate The Kitten Who Wouldn't Purr, Spelling List, Moona Park, The Wise Old Judge, The Lazy Boy,	**Level 2** Boa Constrictor and other Crushing Poems, **Level 3** From Tiger to Anasi,	**Level 3** Dee-ree-ree and the Rainbow, **Level 4** The Stolen Pumpkin, Draw Cats,	**Level 4** Albert the Seagull,	**Level 3** Mind in the Frying Pan, **Level 4** Longneck's Billabong,

S

Title and Publisher	PHASE*	INTEREST AGE	Reading Level A 5^{0}-5^{5}	B 5^{6}-5^{11}	C 6^{0}-6^{5}	D 6^{6}-6^{11}
Storyline (O/P) Oliver and Boyd	P	8 - 12				
Story of Britain (O/P) Ginn	P/S	8 - 12				
Story Poems (O/P) Ginn	P	6 - 9				
Storytrails Cambridge University Press	S	12+				
Storyworlds Heinemann (T, S, RR)	P	4 - 6	**Stage 1** **Our World** (4 titles), **Animal World** (4 titles), **Fantasy World** (4 titles), **Once-upon-a-Time World** (4 titles),	**Stage 2** **Our World** (4 titles), **Animal World** (4 titles), **Once-upon-a-Time World** (4 titles), **Fantasy World** (4 titles), **Stage 3** **Our World** (4 titles), **Animal World** (4 titles), **Once-upon-a-Time World** (4 titles), **Fantasy World** (4 titles),	**Stage 4** **Our World** (4 titles), **Animal World** (4 titles), **Once-upon-a-Time World** (4 titles), **Fantasy World** (4 titles),	**Stage 5** **Our World** (4 titles), **Animal World** (4 titles), **Once-upon-a-Time World** (4 titles), **Fantasy World** (4 titles),
Straws (O/P) LDA	S	11 - 16			**Green:** What a Day!, Mick's Bike, Spooky Night, Death Ride,	
Structural Readers Longman	S	11 - 16				**Stage 1:** Car Thieves, Detectives Gary's First Season,

E 7^{0}-7^{5}	F 7^{6}-7^{11}	G 8^{0}-8^{5}	H 8^{6}-8^{11}	I 9^{0}-9^{5}	J 9^{6}-9^{11}	K 10^{0}-10^{5}+
	Series 1 Ireland, Wildlife, History,	**Series 2** Ireland, Wildlife, History,	**Series 3** Ireland, Wildlife, History,		**Series 4** Ireland, Wildlife, History,	
			1. Early Britain, 2. Britain in the Middle Ages, 3. Tudors, Stuarts and Georgians (O/P), 4. From Nelson to the Present Day (O/P),			
			(8 titles) Remember, Our House, etc.			
				The Evil of Mr. Happiness, The Stone of Badda, Invitation to Murder, Terror in the Fourth Dimension, The King's Mission, The Haunters of Marsh Hall, etc.		
Stage 6 **Our World** (4 titles), **Animal World** (4 titles), **Once-upon-a-Time World** (4 titles), **Fantasy World** (4 titles),						
Blue: Good Dog Laddie, Chicken, The Big Race, How to Lose Your Girl,		**Magenta:** Playing with Guns, Witches, Mark's Rescue, High Jinks,		**Red:** Taffy, Krissie Goes to the Circus, Mark's Paper Round, Trouble at Somer-Leyton,		**Brown:** Ice-Cream in Chapel, The Accident, Secret Agent, Getting Away,
from Scotland Yard, etc.	**Stage 3:** Mosquito Town, Clint Magee, etc.		**Stage 5:** One True Friend, Stories from Down Under, etc.			
Stage 2: April Fools' Day, First Case, etc.		**Stage 4:** Me, Myself and I, The Thirty Nine Steps, etc.		**Stage 6:** Modern Short Stories, The L-Shaped Room, etc.		

S

Title and Publisher	PHASE*	INTEREST AGE	Reading Level **A** 5^0-5^5	**B** 5^6-5^{11}	**C** 6^0-6^5	**D** 6^6-6^{11}
S **Sunshine** Heinemann *[also see New Sunshine on pages 94 and 95.]*	P	4 - 10+	**Sunrise** Animals, Me!, Families, Birthday Party, Space, Friends, School, Shopping, Playing Games, Transport, Eating Out, I Can Read,			
			Sunshine Stories Level 1 **Set A:** 8 titles Baby Gets Dressed, Huggie's Breakfast, etc. **Set B:** 8 titles Snap, My Puppy, etc.		**Sunshine Stories Level 1** **Set C:** 8 titles When Itchy Witch Sneezes, Buzzing Flies, **Set D:** 8 titles I Can Jump, Up In a Tree, etc., **Set E:** 8 titles Spider, Spider, Let's Have a Swim, etc., **Set G:** 8 titles My Boat, The Cooking Pot, etc.,	**Set E:** 9 titles Bread, The Seed, etc.
					← **Set H:** 8 titles The Giant Boy, Ratty-Tatty, etc., →	
						Set I: 8 titles When Dad Went to Playschool, Letters for Mr. James, etc. **Set J:** 8 titles Boring Old Bed, Space Race, etc.,

<table>
<tr><th>E
7^{0}-7^{5}</th><th>F
7^{6}-7^{11}</th><th>G
8^{0}-8^{5}</th><th>H
8^{6}-8^{11}</th><th>I
9^{0}-9^{5}</th><th>J
9^{6}-9^{11}</th><th>K
10^{0}-10^{5}+</th></tr>
<tr><td></td><td>Level 1 Non-Fiction
24 titles
Are You a Ladybird?,
Clouds,
Underwater Journey,
A Small World, etc.,

Level 2: Set B
Rubbish,
Grizzly and the Bumble Bee, etc.,</td><td>Level 2: Set A
The Train Ride,
The Giant Pumpkin,
etc.,</td><td></td><td></td><td></td><td></td></tr>
<tr><td></td><td colspan="2">Level 2: Non-Fiction
It's Not the Same,
Did You Know?,
Animal Pets, etc.,</td><td></td><td></td><td></td><td></td></tr>
<tr><td></td><td>Level 3: Set A
Christmas Day,
The Person from Planet X,
Silly Billy's, etc.,
Set B:
The Gingerbread Man,
Sloppy Tiger and The Party, etc.,</td><td>Level 3: Non-Fiction
The Bugs Bus,
The Waterhole,
Going to Be … A Butterfly, etc.,</td><td></td><td></td><td></td><td></td></tr>
<tr><td></td><td colspan="2">Level 4: Set A
In the Middle of the Night,
Dragon with a Cold, etc.,
Set B:
Jim's Trumpet,
The Mersey Ferry Pidgeon, etc.,</td><td>Level 4: Non-Fiction
A Rocket Surprise,
Joy Cowley Writes, etc.,</td><td></td><td></td><td></td></tr>
<tr><td></td><td>Level 5: Plays
Shopping,
The Norse Festival,</td><td>Level 5: Set A
Morning Bath,
Cousin Kira, etc.,
Set B:
Bunlakkit,
The New Car, etc.,</td><td colspan="2">Level 5: Non-Fiction
The Humpback Whale,
Knights in Armour,
No Place Like Home, etc.,</td><td></td><td></td></tr>
<tr><td></td><td>Level 6: Plays
King of the Beasts,
The Gonks and the Troll,</td><td>Level 6: Set A
The Trouble with Heathrow,
The Pop Group,
Baby's Breakfast, etc.,
Set B:
Lost Property,
Truth, etc.,</td><td></td><td></td><td></td><td></td></tr>
<tr><td></td><td>Level 7: Plays
Presents,
All at Sea,</td><td>Level 7: Set A
The Garden Party,
The Tree Doctor, etc.,</td><td>Level 7: Set B
Anak the Brave,
Hair Restorer, etc.,</td><td></td><td></td><td></td></tr>
<tr><td></td><td>Level 8: Plays
In the Dark,
Ze King Shall Sing,</td><td>Level 8: Set A
A Pet to the Vet,
The New House Villain, etc.,</td><td>Level 8: Set B
Leap Year,
Tiger, etc.,</td><td></td><td></td><td></td></tr>
<tr><td></td><td></td><td colspan="2">Level 9: Set A
Tai Taylor Is Born,
The Terrible Topsy Turvy, etc.,</td><td colspan="2">Level 9: Set B
The Little Round Husband,
Agatha's Brew, etc.,</td><td></td></tr>
<tr><td></td><td></td><td></td><td colspan="2">Level 10: Set B
The Best Diver in the World,
The Boomer Zoomer, etc.,</td><td>Level 10: Set A
Tai Taylor and the Sweet Annie,
The King's Jokes, etc.,</td><td></td></tr>
<tr><td></td><td></td><td></td><td>Level 10: Plays
Master Curl,
Weekend,

Level 11: Plays
Elliott and the Kelly Cats,
Eating Out,</td><td></td><td>Level 11: Set A
The Mad Puppet,
Iris La Bonga and the Helpful Taxi Driver, etc.,
Set B:
Pupil, Time Warp, etc.,</td><td></td></tr>
<tr><td></td><td></td><td></td><td colspan="2">Myths and Legends Starter Pack
The Secret Name of Ra,
Odysseus and the Cyclops,
The Pomegranate Seeds,
Beowulf and the Dragon,
Daughter of the Sun,
Kintu's Mistake,
Androcles and the Lion,
The Theft of Thor's Hammer,
Arthur Becomes King,
Feather-Snake,
Fine!,
The Bharunda Bird,</td><td></td><td></td></tr>
</table>

S

Title and Publisher	PHASE*	INTEREST AGE	Reading Level A 5^0-5^5	B 5^6-5^{11}	C 6^0-6^5	D 6^6-6^{11}
New Sunshine Heinemann *[also see Sunshine on pages 92 and 93. New Sunshine has been included here because it extends Sunshine and the two are together in the catalogue.]*	P	4 - 11	**Emergent - Key Words** **Spiral Starters** ← **Sets A-D** (40 books) →			
			Spirals ← **Sets 1-2** (20 books) →		← **Sets 3 and 4** (20 books) →	← **Stages 5 and 6**
			Emergent Fiction Stories **Set A** (6 books), **Set B** (6 books), **Set C** (6 books), **Set D** (6 books), **Set E** (6 books),	**Set F** (8 books), **Set G** (8 books), **Set H** (8 books),	**Set I** (8 books), **Set J** (8 books),	
		6 - 8	**Early Fluency**			
		8 - 11	**Fluency**			
Study Reading Schofield and Sims	P/S	6 - 15			**Module A** Antelope	**Module B** Bear
Sunstart Reading Scheme Ladybird	P	5 - 10	1. Lucky Dip ← Workbook A →	← 2. On the beach →		3. The Kite, ← Workbook B
Superchamp Books Heinemann	P/S	8 - 12				
Swashbucklers Ginn	P	6 - 8			**Jib the Pirate Monkey** The Rock, The Cook, The Cannon, The Rain, The Storm, The Map,	**Wilf the Cabin Boy** Going Ashore, In Charge, Paint Pots, Birthday Party, Treasure Chest, Pirate Attack,

S

E 7^{0}-7^{5}	F 7^{6}-7^{11}	G 8^{0}-8^{5}	H 8^{6}-8^{11}	I 9^{0}-9^{5}	J 9^{6}-9^{11}	K 10^{0}-10^{5}+
(20 books) →	**Set 7** The Horse, Flying with Tommy,	Locked Out, The Pelican, There's a Dragon in my Garden, Tim, The Museum, **Set 8** The Mouse Box, The Six Little Pigeons, The Old Green Machine, I Spy,	Mrs. Grimble's Grapevine, Bother Those Barnetts!, Mrs. Harriet's Hairdo,	The Bag of Smiles, Brutus, The Echo, The Traveller and the Farmer,	Bees, The Vesper's Boat,	
Adventure Novels Pack (E–F) (from **Level 2**) Mutt and the Lifeguards, Snake!,	(from **Levels 2-5**) Dayton and the Happy Tree, The Little Firefighter, The Robber, The Little Whale, Winklepoo the Wicked, Emma, the Birthday Clown, **Adventure Stories Level 5** (8 books) **Adventure Stories Level 6** (6 books)	**Adventure Stories Level 7** (6 books)	**Non-Fiction Pack** (H–I) (Levels 2-5) Umbrellas, Crabs, Build, Build, Build, At the Edge of the Sea, Boats Afloat, Bird Behaviour, Birds of the City, The Story of You,	**Adventure Stories** (I–K) Level 8 (6 books)		
	Adventure Novels Pack - Levels 6-9 (F–G) The Treasure of the Stone Lions, Dragon Fire, Manda's Mystery, Adventure of Jessica and Zebedee,	Arnold the Ace, The Happy Hackers, Five Strange Packages,		Where Dragons Dance, A Pony for Penny, All About Bicycles,	The Mysterious Dr Clem, Out of the Sunless Land, **Non-Fiction (from Levels 6-11)** (J–K) Margaret Mahy, Masters of the Deep, Shipwrecks, Sweets,	Spikes, Pop Corn, Ice Cream, Chocolate, The Drum, Ancient Man of the Ice,
Module C (E–F) Crocodile	**Module E** (F–G) Elephant		**Module F** Frog	**Module G** Goldfinch	**Module H** Horse	**Module I** Iris **Module J** Jaguar **Module K** Kangaroo **Module L** Lion **Module M** Mole **Module N** Nightingale
4. Animals, Birds and Fish, →	5. I Wish, Workbook C (F–G)	6. Guess What?,				
		Dog Powder, Rosie and the Boredom Eater, How Alice Saved Captain Miracle, All the Kings and Queens, The Egg Timer, A Case of Blue Murder, Sharp Eyes,	The Walloping Stick War, Daljit and the Unqualified Wizard, Crash!,	The Stone Boy, The Boy With His Leg in the Air, The Thursday Creature, Tough as Old Boots, A Spook at the Superstore,	Now You See it..., The Man of the House, Naomi's Secret, Blood Brothers, Thunderpumps,	Mark England's Cap, Size Twelve, The Great Boneshaker Bike,
The Crew The Captain's Story, Gromet's Story, D'Bloons Story, Hue's Story, The Cook's Story, Tom and Harry's Story,						

T

Title and Publisher	PHASE*	INTEREST AGE	Reading Level A 5^{0}-5^{5}	B 5^{6}-5^{11}	C 6^{0}-6^{5}	D 6^{6}-6^{11}
Take Part Ward Lock *[A series of short plays. Each part requires a different reading level from about 6 - 9.6.]*	P/S	**Main Series** 7 - 12 **Starters** 6 - 9			**Take Part Starters:** 18 titles The Clever Little Tailor, How Rabbit **Take Part Tales** The Ugly **Main Series** Beaverbird, Brer Rabbit, Chitty-Chitty- The Last of the Mohicans, Treasure Island,	
Tales and Adventures (O/P) Stanley Thornes	P	6 - 11				
Tales from Hans Anderson Ginn	P	7 - 10				
Tales from Long Ago Ginn	P	7 - 10				
Talespinners (HI-LO Books) (O/P) LDA	S	11 - 16				
Teenage Twelve Gibson	S	12 - 15				
Tell All About It (O/P) Ginn	P	5 - 7+				Look What I've Done Gran, Flying into the Flowerbed, Hide and Seek, Looking after Mum, I Wobbled..., Stop It!...,
'10' Books (O/P) Hodder and Stoughton	S	11 - 15				
That's Another Story (O/P) Hodder and Stoughton	P/S	10 - 13+				
Then and Now (O/P) Ginn	P/S	8 - 12				

E 7^{0}-7^{5}	F 7^{6}-7^{11}	G 8^{0}-8^{5}	H 8^{6}-8^{11}	I 9^{0}-9^{5}	J 9^{6}-9^{11}	K 10^{0}-10^{5}+
Lost his Tail, etc., → **for Two** Duckling, → 7 titles Bang-Bang, Four Stories from Grimm, Children of the New Forest, etc., →						
Tales The Prince and the Nut Tree, The Fisherman and the Seal Woman, The Kingdom under the Sea, When the Clouds Come Down, The Boy with the Geese, The Dragon of the Seven Hills, ← →		**Adventures** The Wild Horse, Rark and the Tiger, The Indian Boy and the Bear, In the Northland, Across the Sea, On the Mountain, ← →				
	1 - 4: The Emperor's New Clothes, The Ugly Duckling, The Nightingale, Dan the Dunce, ← → 5 - 8: The Wild Swans, Thumbelina, The Little Tin Soldiers, The Flying Trunk					
		1 - 8: The Giraffe Who Could Not Walk, The Jar of Bees, The Chest of Gold, The Field of Carrots, The Discontented Pig, Charlie and the Cuckoo, The Great Magician, Alfredo and the Stone, ← → 9 - 16: Parrot Talk, The Three Brothers, Bags of Money, The Crooked Staff, The Two Windmills, The North Wind, The Great Wall, Ellie and Leo, ← →				
				Golden God, A Question of Freedom, Better than New, Out of this World, The Joker, Man in the Cage, Johnny Tail Dog, The Poison Pen Mystery, ← →		
1. Youth Club, 2. Beach Days,	3. Fun Fair, 4. Firefighters, 5. Man on the Beat,	6. A New Games Shed, 7. Sports Day, 8. At the Farm, 9. Away Match, 10. Day Trippers, 11. Behind the Scenes, 12. In the Nick of Time, ← →				
		10 Ghosts, 10 Strange Tales, 10 Monsters of Myth and Legend,				
← Book 1 →		← Book 2 →		← Book 3 and 4 →		
	The Miner, The Driver, The Farmer, The Shopworker, The Potter, The District Nurse, The Sailor, The Teacher, ← →					

T

Title and Publisher	PHASE*	INTEREST AGE	Reading Level A 5^0-5^5	B 5^6-5^{11}	C 6^0-6^5	D 6^6-6^{11}
Thin King Story Books Longman *[A phonic series.]*	P	7 - 10				Books 1 - 4
The '13' Series Hodder and Stoughton	S	5 - 10				
Through the Rainbow Schofield and Sims *[Will be discontinued as stocks become exhausted.]*	P	5 - 10	**The Picture Books** Book 1 ◄── **Red** 1. My House, 2. The Play House, 3. Under the Table, ──► ◄── **Running Along Books** **Red:** 3 titles ──►	Book 2 Book 3 ◄── **Orange** 1. Me and My Toys, 2. Helping and Playing, 3. My School, ──► ◄── **Orange:** 3 titles ──►	Book 4 Book 5 **Yellow** 1. What Can You Make? 2. The Princess and the Giant, 3. I Like the Toy Shop, **Yellow:** 3 titles	Book 6 **Green** 1. The Long Train, 2. Let's Play Shops, 3. The Princess in the Castle, **Blue** 1. Simon and Elizabeth, 2. Days at School, 3. Out to Play, **Green:** 3 titles **Blue:** 3 titles
Thunder the Dinosaur (O/P) Ginn	P	6 - 10				
Tiddlywinks (Nelson) Kingscourt Publishing (T, RR)	P	6 - 9	**Big Books** **Set 1:** 6 titles Cat and Mouse, Wiggly Work, etc., **Set 2:** 6 titles Rat-a-tat-tat, Guinea Pig Grass, etc., **Large Read-Together Books** **Set 1:** 6 titles **Set 2:** 6 titles *[same titles as Big Books.]*			**Small Format Story Books - Stage 1** Grandma's Bicycle, The Amazing Poppy Seed, What Are You Going to Buy?, Cow Up a Tree, Do-Whackey-d, Jessie's Flower, **Stage 3** A Walk with Grandpa, **Stage 4** The Long Grass of Tumbledown Road, Mr. Beep, **Stage 5** A Not-so-quiet Evening, Beautiful Pig, **Stage 7** Jack, the Junk Shop Man, The Bull and the Matador, The Great Pumpkin Battle,

E 7^{0}-7^{5}	F 7^{6}-7^{11}	G 8^{0}-8^{5}	H 8^{6}-8^{11}	I 9^{0}-9^{5}	J 9^{6}-9^{11}	K 10^{0}-10^{5}+
Books 5 - 8	Books 9 - 12	Books 13 - 16				
				13. Ghosts, 13. Horror Stories, 13. Weird Tales, 13. Sci-Fi Stories, 13. Sport and Leisure, 13. Sinister Stories, 13. Compuer Tales, 13. Family Stories, 13. Animal Stories, 13. Tales of Crime,		
Book 7 **Silver** 1. Rainbow's End, ← 2. Wind in the Trees, → **Gold** 1. Firelight and Candlelight, **Indigo** 1. All through the Day, 2. In the Park, 3. Sea and Sand, **Violet** 1. Making Things Is Fun, 2. Paper Boats and Paddling, 3. Simon's Book, **Indigo:** 3 titles **Violet:** 3 titles	Book 8 2. Moonshine and Magic, **Rainbow** 1. The Friendly Farmer, 2. Elephants and Lions, 3. Christmas Time, ← **Jumping Off Books** 1 - 6 → **Rainbow:** 3 titles	Book 9 3. Elflight and Taperlight, 3. Hey Diddle Dumpling,	Book 10 Book 11 4. Early One Morning, ← 4. Starlight and Sunshine, →	Book 12 5. Kings, Princesses and Witches, 6. They Were Brave, 5. Thistledown and Cobweb,	6. Long Ago and Yesterday,	
1. The Egg, 2. Thunder Eats a Haystack, 3. Thunder Gets a House, 4. Thunder Goes to a Party, ← 5. Thunder at the Seaside, → 6. Thunder to the Rescue, 7. Thunder and the Dinofair, 8. Thunder Goes to the Circus,						
The Kangaroo from Woolloomooloo,		The Yukadoos,				
Stage 2 Monster, That's Really Weird, The Difficult Day, The Wild Woolly Child, Let's Get a Pet, What Would I Do?,		Ten Loopy Caterpillars, The Terrible Armadillo,				
The Horrible Thing…, The Fight on the Hill, The Shoe Grabber, Mr. Wumple's Travels,					**Stage 3** Morning Dance,	
The Smile, Arguments, The Frown,	The Adventures of a Kite, The Train that Ran Away,	A Silly Old Story, Mouse Monster,				
Sophie's Singing Mother, As Luck Would Have It, Robber Pig and the Ginger Beer, Robber Pig and the Green Eggs,	The Plant of My Aunt,	The Crocodile's Teeth,	The Earthquake,			
Stage 6 The Mouse Wedding, Tiny Tinny Teaker, Squeak in the Gate,	Lavender the Library Cat, The Wonder Whizz,	Sarah, the Bear and the Kangaroo, The Cake, The Catten,	Strike Me Down…,			
	Clever Hamburger,	The Conversation, A Very Happy Birthday,	How Mr. Rooster Didn't Get Married,			

Title and Publisher	*PHASE**	*INTEREST AGE*	Reading Level A 5^0-5^5	B 5^6-5^{11}	C 6^0-6^5	D 6^6-6^{11}
Tigers Anderson Press	P	7 - 11				
Tim Books (formerly **Flightpath to Reading**) Nelson	P/S	7 - 14				
Tim Paperbacks Nelson	P/S	9 - 14				
Time Detectives (O/P) Nelson *[A history series.]*	P/S	7 - 14				
Time for Reading (O/P) Ginn	P	5 - 9	**Picture Book** **Picture Book Workout**	**Stage 2** The Cherry Family, Quickies: 8 titles	**Stage 3** Penny's Birthday, Story Books 1 - 6, The Naughty Twins, etc.,	**Stage 4** Penny at School, Story Books 7 - 12, Grandpa's Greenhouse, etc., **Stage 5** The Bread and Butter House
Tintin (O/P) Methuen	P/S	7 - 14				
Traditional Tales from Around the World Ginn	P/S	9 - 14				
Trend Books (original series) Ginn	S	12 - 16				**Approach Trend** Godfrey, Night Cats, That Old Tin Can, Last Train, Pigs and Things, I Like Me, Walk in the Sun, **Trend** The Dark House, Wild Dog, It Happened on Saturday, Go Home Kid, Danger Ride, Why Penny White Lie, Sudden

The NASEN A–Z: A Graded List of Reading Books

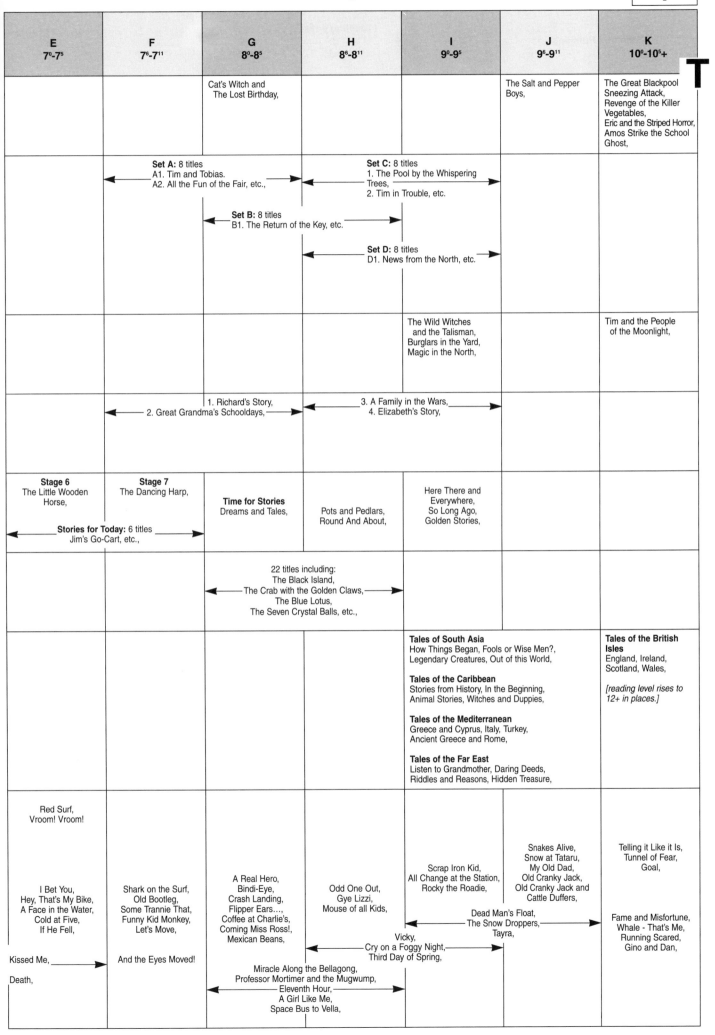

T

E 7^{0}-7^{5}	F 7^{6}-7^{11}	G 8^{0}-8^{5}	H 8^{6}-8^{11}	I 9^{0}-9^{5}	J 9^{6}-9^{11}	K 10^{0}-10^{5}+
		Cat's Witch and The Lost Birthday,			The Salt and Pepper Boys,	The Great Blackpool Sneezing Attack, Revenge of the Killer Vegetables, Eric and the Striped Horror, Amos Strike the School Ghost,
	Set A: 8 titles A1. Tim and Tobias. A2. All the Fun of the Fair, etc.,	**Set B:** 8 titles B1. The Return of the Key, etc.	**Set C:** 8 titles 1. The Pool by the Whispering Trees, 2. Tim in Trouble, etc. **Set D:** 8 titles D1. News from the North, etc.			
				The Wild Witches and the Talisman, Burglars in the Yard, Magic in the North,		Tim and the People of the Moonlight,
	1. Richard's Story, 2. Great Grandma's Schooldays,		3. A Family in the Wars, 4. Elizabeth's Story,			
Stage 6 The Little Wooden Horse, **Stories for Today:** 6 titles Jim's Go-Cart, etc.,	**Stage 7** The Dancing Harp,	**Time for Stories** Dreams and Tales,	Pots and Pedlars, Round And About,	Here There and Everywhere, So Long Ago, Golden Stories,		
		22 titles including: The Black Island, The Crab with the Golden Claws, The Blue Lotus, The Seven Crystal Balls, etc.,				
				Tales of South Asia How Things Began, Fools or Wise Men?, Legendary Creatures, Out of this World, **Tales of the Caribbean** Stories from History, In the Beginning, Animal Stories, Witches and Duppies, **Tales of the Mediterranean** Greece and Cyprus, Italy, Turkey, Ancient Greece and Rome, **Tales of the Far East** Listen to Grandmother, Daring Deeds, Riddles and Reasons, Hidden Treasure,		**Tales of the British Isles** England, Ireland, Scotland, Wales, *[reading level rises to 12+ in places.]*
Red Surf, Vroom! Vroom! I Bet You, Hey, That's My Bike, A Face in the Water, Cold at Five, If He Fell, Kissed Me, Death,	Shark on the Surf, Old Bootleg, Some Trannie That, Funny Kid Monkey, Let's Move, And the Eyes Moved!	A Real Hero, Bindi-Eye, Crash Landing, Flipper Ears..., Coffee at Charlie's, Coming Miss Ross!, Mexican Beans, Miracle Along the Bellagong, Professor Mortimer and the Mugwump, Eleventh Hour, A Girl Like Me, Space Bus to Vella,	Odd One Out, Gye Lizzi, Mouse of all Kids, Vicky, Cry on a Foggy Night, Third Day of Spring,	Scrap Iron Kid, All Change at the Station, Rocky the Roadie, Dead Man's Float, The Snow Droppers, Tayra,	Snakes Alive, Snow at Tataru, My Old Dad, Old Cranky Jack, Old Cranky Jack and Cattle Duffers,	Telling it Like it Is, Tunnel of Fear, Goal, Fame and Misfortune, Whale - That's Me, Running Scared, Gino and Dan,

T

Title and Publisher	PHASE*	INTEREST AGE	Reading Level A 5^0-5^5	B 5^6-5^{11}	C 6^0-6^5	D 6^6-6^{11}
Trend Facts Ginn	S	11 - 16+				
Trog Nelson	P/S	7 - 14				
Twists Hodder and Stoughton	S	11 - 16				

U

Upstarts (Reading 360) Ginn (S)	P S P	6 - 10 13 - 16+ 5 - 8		**Introductory Level** What's in the Box?, Tim's Surprise, There's Paul, The Race, The Clever Cat, Debbie and the Mouse,		**Level 1** 1. There's a Monster, 2. Paul and the Robber, 3. Look at My Spots, 4. The Rabbit Said Miaow, 5. Lucy the Tiger, 6. The Goat Is Eating Debbie, **Level 1 Extension Books** 1a. Bobby Bear and the Rabbit, 2a. Peg and the Fair, 3a. The Shoes Had Spots, 4a. Jan and Dan, 5a. Where Is Fred Dragon?, 1b. Jan and the Monster, 2b. Cat and Mouse, 3b. Jenny and the Dragon, 4b. The Queen and the Cabbage, 5b. The Balloons, 6b. The King's Box, **Level 3** Lucy Calls James and Pippa and Naughty Babies are The Fat **Level 3 Extension** The Apple Sunil's Bad Fun at Helpful Circus Pancake

T

E 7^{0}-7^{5}	F 7^{6}-7^{11}	G 8^{0}-8^{5}	H 8^{6}-8^{11}	I 9^{0}-9^{5}	J 9^{6}-9^{11}	K 10^{0}-10^{5}+
			The Eye,	Bushrangers, Fantastic Pets, Vikings, Stargazing, Windsurfing, Helicopters, Flying High, Out of This World, Whale Wonder, Sharks, Skydiving, Working Underwater, Drawing with Light,	TV - Behind the Scenes, About the Heart, Genes, World Tour,	
That Boy Trog Trog and his Axe, Trog and the Fire, Trog and his Boat, Trog and the Dog, **Trog and Grandpa Gripe** Grandpa Tells a Story, Grandpa Goes Fishing, Trog and the Snowman, Trog and the Letter, etc., (8 titles) **That Boy Trog Again** Grandpa and the Robbers, Grandpa by the Sea, Grandpa's Band, The Visit, The Game, Grandpa's Dream, The Ghost Grandpa Makes a Cake,	Trog Makes a Trap, Grandpa Has a Swim, Grandpa and the Horse, Grandpa Plays Hide and Seek,	**Trog's Grandpa Knows Best** Grandpa's Horse Race, Grandpa and the Mammoth, Grandpa the Birdman, Grandpa Goes Hunting,				
		Twists, A Twist in the Tale, Twist and Turn,				

U

E 7^{0}-7^{5}	F 7^{6}-7^{11}	G 8^{0}-8^{5}	H 8^{6}-8^{11}	I 9^{0}-9^{5}	J 9^{6}-9^{11}	K 10^{0}-10^{5}+
Level 2 1. The Clever Beetle, 2. Rum Tum Tum, 3. Kate and Debbie…, 4. The New Bike, 5. The Runaway Pram, 6. The Ghost Behind the Cupboard, **Level 2 Extension Books** 1a. The Greedy Parrot, 2a. Don't Eat the Postman, 3a. The Clever Ghost, 4a. The Toy Ship, 5a. No Dogs Allowed, 6a. The Silly Elephant, 1b. The Clever Mouse, 2b. The Surprise, 3b. I Like Space Ships, 4b. Mum's New Car, 5b. The Unhappy Giant, 6b. The Monster in the Cupboard, the Fire Brigade, the Dragon, the Witch, → Norman, Yuk, Cat, **Books** Tree, Dream, the Zoo, → Hannah, Tricks, Day, **Level 4** Aunt Horrible…, Emily the Spy, The Magic Carrot, Not-so-Silly Billy, Toby and the Space Cats, Molly and the Giant,	**Level 4 Extension Books** The Cheese that Disappeared, The Best Watchdog in the World, Nancy and the Giant Spotted Newt, Sandy and the Snowball, Monty and the Monster Mouse, Dennis and the Dinosaur,					

V

Title and Publisher	PHASE*	INTEREST AGE	Reading Level A 5^0-5^5	B 5^6-5^{11}	C 6^0-6^5	D 6^6-6^{11}
Vardo Series Hodder and Stoughton	P/S	10 - 15				
Vowel Crowd, The (O/P) Heinemann	P/S	10 - 15				

W

Title and Publisher	PHASE*	INTEREST AGE	Reading Level A 5^0-5^5	B 5^6-5^{11}	C 6^0-6^5	D 6^6-6^{11}
War at Home Heinemann	P/S	10 - 16				
Watching Books (O/P) Ginn	P	7 - 12				
Wellington Square Nelson (T, S, IT)		7 - 13+	**Level 1** **Picture Books** Moving In, Rocky and Friends, Rocky at School, Mr. Keeping, Into the Water, A Birthday Bonfire,			**Level 2** What a Goal!, The Rainbow Wall, The Yellow Canary, The Moving Statue, Hot Stuff, The Trampoline,
Well-Loved Tales (Series 606D) Ladybird	P	7 - 10				
Wesley and the Dinosaurs Ginn	P	6 - 9+				
Whatever Next? (O/P) Ginn	P	6 - 9				Susie's Day, Cheeky, Happy Christmas,
What's It Like to Be ... Ginn	P/S	8 - 12				

E 7^0-7^5	F 7^6-7^{11}	G 8^0-8^5	H 8^6-8^{11}	I 9^0-9^5	J 9^6-9^{11}	K 10^0-10^5+	
		1. The Game, 2. The Eye of All Power (O/P), 3. The Silver Cross, 4. The Lord of Space, 5. The Invaders, 6. Last Rays of the Sun, 7. The Glass Prison, 8. The Machines, 9. The Duel, 10. The Hunt, 11. The Staff, the Cloak, and the Dagger, 12. The Final Day,					**V**
	← Book 1	→ ← Book 2	→	(so far)			
				← War at Home, War in Europe,	War in the Far East, →		**W**
	Kestrel, Butterfly, Cat, Dolphin,						
Level 3 Rocky's Fox, Afraid of the Water, What a Mystery, Aliens, Jamila at the Fair, The Bomb Scare,	**Level 4** The Radio Mystery, Danger in the Pond, Prisoners in the Dungeon, The Dragon Kite, Accident, Going for Gold,	**Level 5** Hello France!, Bombs over Wellington Square, The Good Samaritans, Safari Park, Playing Away, Rescue Service,				**Wellington Square Extra** **Phase 1** **Set 1:** Football, Animals, Emergency Services, Australia, Education, Europe, **Set 2:** Photography, TV and Radio, Exploration, World War II, Publishing, Environment, **Phase 2** **Set 1:** Medicine, America, Shops, Primates, Africa, Detectives, **Set 2:** Boats and Canals, The Duke of Wellington, Olympics, Flight, Castles, Asia,	
← Grade 1: 18 titles The Elves and the Shoemaker, The Three Little	Pigs, The Gingerbread Boy, The Big Pancake, etc., → ← Grade 2: 15 titles Sleeping Beauty, Dick Whittington,	Pinocchio, Rapunzel, etc., → ← Grade 3: 13 titles Cinderella, Snow White and Rose Red,	Tom Thumb, The Little Mermaid, etc., →				
	Tyrannosaurus the Terrible, Brachiosaurus in the River, Triceratops on the Farm, Dinosaurs on the Motorway,	A Diplodocus in the Garden,	Pterodactyl at the Airport,				
The New Baby, Locked Out, The Dressing Up Race,							
			← Quentin Blake - Artist, Michael Rosen - Poet,	Trish Cooke - TV Presenter, Jan Hoy - Personnel Officer, →			

W

Title and Publisher	PHASE*	INTEREST AGE	Reading Level A 5^0-5^5	B 5^6-5^{11}	C 6^0-6^5	D 6^6-6^{11}
What's That You're Reading? What the Papers Said Hodder and Stoughton	S	14 - 16+				
Whizz Bang Books (O/P) Longman	P/S	8 - 12				
Wide Range Readers Longman	P/S	5 - 12		**Picture Stories** Red (6 titles) Blue (6 titles) Green (6 titles0		
						Wide Range 1985 Edition
Wide World Black	P/S	7 - 11				
Winners Hodder and Stoughton	P/S	9 - 12				
Word Power Longman	P/S	7 - 11				
Words About Series Hodder and Stoughton	S	13 - 18				
Word Quest LDA	P/S	9 - 15				
World Wildlife (Series S864) (Some O/P) Ladybird	P	7 - 10			Animal Alphabet Book, Birds, Plants O/P, Animals, Animal Homes, ← Our World in Danger O/P, →	

<table>
<tr><th>E
7^0-7^5</th><th>F
7^6-7^{11}</th><th>G
8^0-8^5</th><th>H
8^6-8^{11}</th><th>I
9^0-9^5</th><th>J
9^6-9^{11}</th><th>K
10^0-10^5+</th></tr>
<tr><td></td><td></td><td></td><td></td><td></td><td colspan="2">What the Papers Said,
What's That You're Reading?,</td></tr>
<tr><td colspan="2" rowspan="2">Yellow Level
The Crocodile and the Monkey,
The Monkey Tales, The Mouse and the Treasure,
Grandpa's Long Ride, A Cat Called Rover,</td><td colspan="2">Red Level
Princess Ugly-Face, The Cross Old Man,
How Kilora Became Queen, Clay Horses,
Oliver the Daring Birdman,</td><td colspan="2">Adventures: Discovery in the Antarctic,
Galapagos, Indians in the Painted Desert,
Easter Island, Antarctica,
The Canadian Arctic,</td><td></td></tr>
<tr><td></td><td colspan="2">Green Level
The Green Children of the Woods,
Wild Dog, Trapped, What in the World,</td><td colspan="2">Blue
The Rescue, Globe of Zelkon,</td></tr>
<tr><td rowspan="10"></td><td>Wide Range Readers
(Original edition)</td><td></td><td></td><td></td><td></td><td></td></tr>
<tr><td>Blue Series
Green Series
Red Series
Book 1</td><td>Book
2</td><td>Book
3</td><td>Book
4</td><td>Book
5</td><td>Book
6</td></tr>
<tr><td>Interest 1</td><td>2</td><td>3</td><td>4</td><td></td><td></td></tr>
<tr><td>More Interest</td><td>1</td><td>2</td><td>3</td><td colspan="2">4</td></tr>
<tr><td colspan="2">New Interest 1</td><td colspan="2">2</td><td>3</td><td>4</td></tr>
<tr><td colspan="2">History 1</td><td colspan="2">2</td><td>3</td><td>4</td></tr>
<tr><td colspan="2">World Religions 1</td><td colspan="2">2</td><td>3</td><td>4</td></tr>
<tr><td colspan="2">Myths and Legends 1</td><td colspan="2">2</td><td>3</td><td>4</td></tr>
<tr><td>Early Birds
Red (4 titles)
Blue (6 titles)
Green (6 titles)</td><td></td><td></td><td></td><td></td><td></td></tr>
<tr><td></td><td>Starters
Blue 1
Green 1
Red 1</td><td>Starters
Blue 2
Green 2
Red 2</td><td></td><td></td><td></td></tr>
<tr><td rowspan="2">Readers
Blue 1
Green 1
Red 1</td><td rowspan="2">Blue 2
Green 2
Red 2</td><td rowspan="2">Blue 3
Green 3
Red 3</td><td rowspan="2">Blue 4
Green 4
Red 4</td><td colspan="2">Blue 5
Green 5</td><td rowspan="2">Blue 5
Green 5
Red 7 and 8</td></tr>
<tr><td>Red 5</td><td>Red 6</td></tr>
<tr><td colspan="2">Lost at the Fair, Whatever Next?,
The Very Special Sari, The Perfect Present,
Going Fishing, A Dozen Angels,
The Missing Money, Nazrul's Kite,
The Very Hot Samosas, etc.,</td><td></td><td></td><td></td><td></td><td></td></tr>
<tr><td></td><td colspan="2">Under the Flag,
The Rungal Disc,
The Stone of Sacrifice,
The End of the Rainbow,
Billy's Big Push, Bikes in the Air,
The Magic Football,
The Mystery of the Shadows,</td><td></td><td></td><td></td><td></td></tr>
<tr><td></td><td></td><td>Word Power Starter</td><td>Word Power 1</td><td>Word Power 2</td><td>Word Power 3</td><td>Word Power 4</td></tr>
<tr><td></td><td></td><td></td><td></td><td></td><td colspan="2">Words About Town (O/P),
Words About the House,
Words About Work (O/P),
Words About Our Health,
Read All About It,</td></tr>
<tr><td></td><td></td><td></td><td></td><td>Word Quest</td><td></td><td></td></tr>
<tr><td></td><td></td><td></td><td></td><td></td><td></td><td></td></tr>
</table>

Title and Publisher	PHASE*	INTEREST AGE	Reading Level A 5^0-5^5	B 5^6-5^{11}	C 6^0-6^5	D 6^6-6^{11}
W						
Working Animals (O/P) Black	P	6 - 9				
Y						
Yearling Books Transworld Publishers *[A selection from the many titles available.]*	P/S	9 - 14				
You And Me Storybooks (O/P) Longman	P	5 - 8			The Ugly Duckling, The Three Bears, The Black and White Cat, The Three Little Pigs, The Selfish Twins, Mr. Spot and Mr. Bob, [spans C to D]	
Young Scientist (O/P) Wayland	P/S	8 - 14				
Young Explorer (O/P) Wayland	P/S	8 - 13				
Z						
Zigzags (O/P) Blackwell	P	7 - 11				
Zoo Books (O/P) Ginn	P/S	9 - 14+				
Zoom Ginn *[formerly 'Ziggy Zoom' in the All Aboard Scheme.]* (T, AU)		6 - 8	**Readers** **Set A** The Terrible Twins, Cool! Shoot! Hair!, Money! Money! Money!, Going Fishing, Too Hot!, Open Wide!, [spans A to B] **Set B** Meet Joe, Joe Gets First Prize, Super Granny!, 'Where's My Bike?', Annie's Secret Letters, Billy the Bully, Super Diary!, I Told You So!, [spans A to B]	**Set C** Meet Ziggy, Robber Zoom, Skateboard Zoom, Downhill Zoom, Popstar Zoom, Party Zoom, Danger Zoom, [spans B to C]		

<table>
<tr><th></th><th>E
7^0-7^5</th><th>F
7^6-7^{11}</th><th>G
8^0-8^5</th><th>H
8^6-8^{11}</th><th>I
9^0-9^5</th><th>J
9^6-9^{11}</th><th>K
10^0-10^5+</th></tr>
<tr><td>W</td><td></td><td colspan="2">← Elephant, Guide Dog, Racehorse, Police Horse, Sheepdog, Shire Horse, →</td><td></td><td></td><td></td><td></td></tr>
<tr><td>Y</td><td></td><td>Frog,</td><td>Trouble in the Cupboard,
Sam the Girl Detective,
Poor Badger,</td><td>Room 13,
The Story of Tracy Beaker,</td><td>Gerald and the Pelican,</td><td></td><td>The Creature in the Dark,
Ghost Dog,
A Dragon in Summer,
Count Karlstein,</td></tr>
<tr><td></td><td></td><td></td><td></td><td></td><td></td><td></td><td></td></tr>
<tr><td></td><td></td><td></td><td></td><td colspan="2">← Clocks and Time, Electric Power, Flowers and Plants, Leaves and Ramps, Life in Fresh Water, Reading the Weather, The Seashore, Soil, Solar Power, Touch, Taste and Smell, Trees, Water Power, Wheels, →</td><td></td><td></td></tr>
<tr><td></td><td></td><td></td><td colspan="2">← Around the Coast, Farms and Farming, Hills and Mountains, Maps and Map-Making, Rivers and Streams, Roads, Railways and Canals, Where People Live, Where Plants Grow, →</td><td></td><td></td><td></td></tr>
<tr><td>Z</td><td colspan="2">← The Hedgehog, The Wood Ant, The Frog, The Garden Spider, →</td><td></td><td></td><td></td><td></td><td></td></tr>
<tr><td></td><td></td><td></td><td></td><td></td><td></td><td></td><td>12 titles:
Tiger, Polar Bear, Timber Wolf, Seal, African Elephant, Gorilla, Moose, Hippopotamus, Penguin, Camel, Orangutan, Beaver,</td></tr>
<tr><td></td><td></td><td></td><td></td><td></td><td></td><td></td><td></td></tr>
<tr><td></td><td></td><td></td><td></td><td></td><td></td><td></td><td></td></tr>
<tr><td></td><td></td><td></td><td></td><td></td><td></td><td></td><td></td></tr>
<tr><td></td><td></td><td></td><td></td><td></td><td></td><td></td><td></td></tr>
<tr><td></td><td></td><td></td><td></td><td></td><td></td><td></td><td></td></tr>
</table>

New Titles: A Personal List

Title and Publisher	PHASE*	INTEREST AGE	Reading Level A 5^{0}-5^{5}	B 5^{6}-5^{11}	C 6^{0}-6^{5}	D 6^{6}-6^{11}

E 7^{0}-7^{5}	F 7^{6}-7^{11}	G 8^{0}-8^{5}	H 8^{6}-8^{11}	I 9^{0}-9^{5}	J 9^{6}-9^{11}	K 10^{0}-10^{5}+

New Titles: A Personal List

Title and Publisher	PHASE*	INTEREST AGE	Reading Level A 5^0-5^5	B 5^6-5^{11}	C 6^0-6^5	D 6^6-6^{11}

E 7^{0}-7^{5}	F 7^{6}-7^{11}	G 8^{0}-8^{5}	H 8^{6}-8^{11}	I 9^{0}-9^{5}	J 9^{6}-9^{11}	K 10^{0}-10^{5}+

Publishers' Addresses

AMS Educational
Woodside Trading Estate
Low Lane
Horsforth
Leeds
LS18 5NY
Tel: 0113 258 0309

Anderson Press
20 Vauxhall Bridge Road
London
SW1V 2SA
Tel: 0171 973 9000

Anglia Young Books
Durham's Farmhouse
Butcher's Hill
Ickleton
Saffron Walden
Essex
CB10 1SR
Tel: 01799 531192

Ann Arbor Publishers Ltd
PO Box 1
Belford
Northumberland
NE70 7JX
Tel: 01668 214460

A & C Black
Howard Road
Eaton Socon
Huntingdon
Cambridgeshire
PE19 3EZ
Tel: 01480 212666

Basic Skills Agency
(formerly ALBSU)
Commonwealth House
1-19 New Oxford Street
London
WC1A 1NU
Tel: 0171 405 4017

Cambridge University Press
The Edinburgh Building
Shaftsbury Road
Cambridge
CB2 2RU
Tel: 01223 325013

Cherrytree Press Ltd
Windsor Bridge Road
Bath
Avon
BA2 3AX

Collins Educational
77-85 Fulham Palace Road
Hammersmith
London
W6 8JB
Tel: 0181 307 4768

Robert Gibson and Sons (Glasgow) Ltd
17 Fitzroy Place
Glasgow
G3 7BR
Tel: 0141 248 5674

Ginn & Co
Prebendal House
Parson's Fee
Aylesbury
HP20 2QZ
Tel: 01296 88411

Heinemann Educational
Halley Court
Jordan Hill
Oxford
OX2 8EJ
Tel: 01865 314333

Hodder & Stoughton
388 Euston Road
London
NW1 3BH
Tel: 0171 873 6250

Kingscourt Publishing Ltd
PO Box 1427
FREEPOST
London
W6 9BR
Tel: 0181 741 2533

Ladybird Books
PO Box 12
Beeches Road
Loughborough
LE11 2NQ
Tel: 01509 268021

LDA
Duke Street
Wisbech
PE13 2AE
Tel: 01945 587361

Learning Materials Ltd
Dixon Street
Wolverhampton
WV2 2BX
Tel: 01902 454026

Longman Group
Edinburgh Gate
Harlow
Essex
CM20 2JE
Tel: 01279 623623

Macdonald Young Books
(see Wayland Publishers)

Methuen Children's Books
38 Hans Crescent
London
SW1X 0LZ
Tel: 0171 581 9393

Mills and Boon
17-19 Foley Street
London
W1A 1DR
Tel: 0181 948 0444

John Murray Publishers Ltd
50 Albermarle Street
London
W1X 4BD
Tel: 0171 493 4361

NASEN Enterprises Ltd
NASEN House
4/5 Amber Business Village
Amber Close
Tamworth
B77 4RP
Tel: 01827 311500

Thomas Nelson & Sons
Nelson House
Mayfield Road
Walton-on-Thames
KT12 5PL
Tel: 01932 262234

James Nisbet & Co. Ltd
78 Tilehouse Street
Hitchin
Hertfordshire
SG5 2DY
Tel: 01462 438331

Oxford University Press
Walton Street
Oxford
OX2 6PD
Tel: 01865 56767

Schofield and Sims
Dogley Mill
Fenay Bridge
Huddersfield
HD8 0NW
Tel: 01484 607080

Scholastic Ltd
Villers House
Clarendon Avenue
Leamington Spa
CV32 5PA
Tel: 01926 887799

Stanley Thornes
Ellenborough House
Wellington Street
Cheltenham
Gloucester
GL50 1YD
Tel: 01242 228888

Transworld Publishers
61-63 Uxbridge Road
London
W5 5SA
Tel: 0181 579 2652

Ward Lock Educational
TR House
1 Christopher Road
East Grinstead
RH19 3BT
Tel: 01342 318 980

The Watts Publishing Group
96 Leonard Street
London
EC2A 4RH
Tel: 0171 739 2929

Wayland Publishers
61 Western Road
Hove
East Sussex
BN3 1JD
Tel: 01273 722561

References and Further Reading

Arnold, H (1982) *Listening to Children Reading,* Hodder and Stoughton: Sevenoaks.

Barrs, M and Thomas, A (eds.) (1991) *The Reading Book,* published by and available from: Centre for Language in Primary Schools, Webber Row, London, SE1 8QW.

Beard, R (1990) *Developing Reading 3-13,* 2nd edition, Hodder and Stoughton: Sevenoaks.

Beverton, S et al (1993) *Running Family Reading Groups,* United Kingdom Reading Association (UKRA): Widnes.

Bloom, W et al (1995) *The Reading Handbook,* Ward Lock Educational: East Grinstead.

Bloom, W, Martin, T, and Waters, M (1988) *Managing to Read,* Collins Educational: Glasgow.

Bormuth, J R (1966) 'Readability: a new approach', *Reading Research Quarterly,* Vol 1, No 3.

DES (1975) *A Language for Life* (The Bullock Report), HMSO.

Fry, E (1968) 'A readability formula that saves time', *Journal of Reading,* Vol 11.

Gains, C and Wray, D (eds.) (1995) *Reading: Issues and Directions,* NASEN Enterprises: Tamworth.

Harrison, C (1980) *Readability in the Classroom,* Cambridge University Press: Cambridge.

Hinson, M and Smith, P (1997) *Phonics and Phonic Resources,* NASEN Enterprises: Tamworth.

Inglis, J (1991) *Choosing and Using Books with Children,* published by and available from Home and School Council, 40, Sunningdale Mount, Sheffield, S11 9HA, priced £1.25, p and p included.

McNicholas, J and McEntee, J (1993) *Games to Improve Reading Levels,* NASEN Enterprises: Tamworth.

Neate, B (1992) *Finding Out About Finding Out,* Hodder and Stoughton: London.

Sawyer, C and Knight, E (1991) 'A fast method for calculating reading levels', *Support for Learning,* Vol 6, No 2.

Smith, D, Shirley, J and Visser, J (1996) *Parents and Teachers: Together for Reading,* NASEN Enterprises: Tamworth.

Wolfendale, S and Bryans, T (1993) *Word Play,* NASEN Enterprises: Tamworth.

Wray, D (1995) *Teaching Information Skills Through Project Work,* Hodder and Stoughton: London.

APPENDIX 1
A Fast Method for Calculating Text Readability Levels

The procedure is relatively simple. The text is read slowly. The space bar is tapped for every single syllable word. If the word has more than one syllable, the space bar is tapped for the first syllable and the return key is tapped for each subsequent one. At the end of each sentence the full stop key is pressed.

The words and sentences are logged on the screen for reference as they are counted. Each key tapped has a different tone to give audible feedback. When the 100-word mark has been exceeded, the computer prints the number of syllables and the number of sentences on the screen. This data can be used to calculate the Fry readability level using the appropriate graph.

The program, for use with the BBC Micro in BBC BASIC, is listed below. Be careful to type it into the computer exactly as listed and then save it on disk or tape for future use.

```
10   MODE7
20   *FX11,0
30   WRD=0:SEN=0:SYL=0:LAST=0
40   PRINT TAB(1,15) “Words counted =”;WRD
50   PRINT TAB(1,17) “Sentences counted =”;SEN
60   G=GET
70   IF G=32 THEN WRD=WRD+1:SYL=SYL+1:SOUND 1,-15,170,1
80   IF G=13 THEN SYL=SYL+1:SOUND 1,-15,145,1
90   IF G=62 OR G=46 THEN SEN=SEN+1: LAST=WRD:SOUND 1,-15,115,1
100  IF WRD=101 THEN 120
110  GOTO 40
120  H=LAST/SEN
130  K=(100-LAST)/H
140  IF K>1 THEN K=1
150  CLS
170  PRINT TAB(1,15) “Words = 100”
180  PRINT TAB(1,17) “Number of sentences =”;SEN+K
190  PRINT TAB(1,19) “Syllables =”;SYL-1
```

Typing in line 160 VDU2 and line 200 VDU1,13,3 would give a hard copy on a printer if one was attached. Anyone with a reasonable knowledge of programming should be able to adapt the program for other formulae which require similar data or for other computers using their own version of BASIC.

It may take two or three samples of text to accustom the user to the method. Trials have shown, however, that using the program can be more than twice as fast as using the original, manual method. The above program may be freely copied and adapted.

APPENDIX 2
Computer Software for Assessing Readability
(All enquiries should be addressed to either the publishers or distributors of these programs.)

Readability Reckoning
Published in 1985 by Arnold Wheaton/AVP. Available from:

AVP Computing,
School Hill Centre,
Chepstow,
Monmouthshire,
NP6 5PH.
Tel: 01291 625439

Price: BBC Disk (5½") £26.95 + VAT.
Acorn Archimedes Disk (3½") £32.50 + VAT.

Disks for BBC B; BBC B+ and BBC 128 computers and Archimedes series.

Useful for: English, reading skills and language work in primary and secondary schools.

Calculates the reading levels of books in the classroom or library.

Readlevel
Published by Daco Software. Available from:

Daco Systems Ltd.,
459-465, Warwick Road,
Tysley,
Birmingham,
B11 2JP.
Tel: 0121 706 8933

Price: £29.95

Disk, user's notes and teacher's notes for BBC B, BBC B+, BBC Master, Acorn A 3000, 4000 and 5000 series and Acorn Archimedes computers.

Useful for: English teaching; reading skills and special educational needs in both primary and secondary schools. This is a program which allows users to assess the readability level of any printed material by typing a selection from the material into the program. The readability display may be screened at any time after completing the first sentence.

Many PC word processor packages such as ***Wordstar, Wordperfect, AmiPro*** and ***MultiMate*** include text grading software. Few give age-related scores but some give American school grade levels.

Other programs for BBC, PC etc., available from:

RICKITT EDUCATIONAL MEDIA
Great Western House
Langport
Somerset
TA10 9YU
Tel: 01458 253636
Fax: 01458 253646
Email: 100647.3472@compuserve.com

SNUG, 39 Ecclestone Gardens, St. Helens, Lancashire, WA10 3BJ.